SUPERCONDUCTIVITY

SUPERCONDUCTIVITY

Proceedings of the Advanced Summer Study
Institute, McGill University, Montreal

Edited by

P. R. WALLACE

Institute of Theoretical Physics
McGill University

Volume 2

GORDON AND BREACH, SCIENCE PUBLISHERS
New York/London/Paris

FOREWORD

The McGill Advanced Summer Study Institute on Superconductivity, which took place from June 17-29, 1968 is the first of what are intended to be annual advanced summer schools sponsored by the Institute of Theoretical Physics of McGill University; the subject will change from year to year. The format of the school was to have series of from three to six lectures covering different topics in superconductivity, (there were seven such series in this case), which were supplemented by more specialized discussions, usually consisting of two lectures each, of special topics. The total number of speakers was nineteen. The somewhat more than 130 participants represented a wide geographical distribution; about one-half were from the United States, and the rest about equally divided between Canada and Europe. The School was, therefore, much more international in character than any previously held in Canada.

I should like to express sincere thanks to all of the speakers. The talks were of consistently high calibre. Their subject matter was in general very timely indeed, and the standard of preparation and exposition exemplary. The excellence of the lectures was reflected in high level of interest of those attending, and the degree of audience participation. Exchange

of ideas was facilitated by the fact that a large portion of the lecturers and "students" were housed in
the same university residence, and several social
"get-togethers" served to break the ice.

Thanks are due to the lecturers for their coop-
eration in preparing the manuscripts from which this
book is published, and to our secretaries, Mrs. Marie
Ange Fyfe, Cheryl Mac Donald and Susan Jensen for
the many tasks which they performed, not the least
being the typing of the proceedings. Very special
mention must be made of the work of Mrs. Fyfe, who
took part in every phase of the organization of the Institute in the months preceding it and who, with un-
failing efficiency and good humour, coped during the
conference with the myriad of problems, both expected and unexpected, which such an enterprise entails.
Not the least of her contributions was to reduce the
burden on the Director to manageable proportions.

The major part of the financial support was provided by the Scientific Council of N.A.T.O., which
made possible, by its generosity, the participation
of such a large number of scientists from overseas.
I should also like to thank the National Research
Council of Canada, the governments of Canada, Que-
bec and France for their assistance under the terms
of existing cultural exchange agreements, and the
Office of Naval Research of the United States, for
providing significant support.

> P. R. Wallace
> Director, Institute of Theoretical
> Physics and Advanced Summer Study
> Institute on Superconductivity,
> McGill University

LIST OF PARTICIPANTS

Dr. V. Ambegaokar   University of Rochester
New York, U.S.A.

Dr. A. Baratoff   Brown University
Rhode Island, U.S.A.

Dr. K. H. Bennemann   University of Rochester
New York, U.S.A.

Dr. Burger   Orsay
France

Dr. J. Carbotte   McGill University
Montreal, Canada

Dr. P. Fulde   Inst. von Laue-Langevin
Germany

Dr. A. Griffin   University of Toronto
Ontario, Canada

Dr. E. Guyon   Orsay
France

Dr. M. A. Jensen   University of Pennsylvania
                        Philadelphia, U.S.A.

Dr. K. Maki   Kyoto
                        Japan

Dr. B. T. Matthias   Lajolla University
                        California, U.S.A.

Dr. R. D. Parks   University of Rochester
                        New York, U.S.A.

Dr. E. R. Pike   Malvern
                        England

Dr. J. M. Rowell   Bell Telephone Lab.
                        Murray Hill, U.S.A.

Dr. A. Schmid   University of Karlsruhe
                        Germany

Dr. M. Stephen   Massachusetts Institute
                        of Technology (M.I.T.)
                        Mass., U.S.A.

Dr. L. Tewordt   University of Hamburg
                        Germany

Dr. M. Tinkham   Harvard University
                        Mass., U.S.A.

CONTENTS

VOLUME 1

VOLUME 2

HIGH FIELD SUPERCONDUCTIVITY

PROXIMITY EFFECTS
OF THICK SUPERCONDUCTING FILM

P. Fulde

HIGH FIELD SUPERCONDUCTIVITY

P. Fulde

Institut für Theoretische Physik
Universität Frankfurt/Main

GENERAL REMARKS

1. What characterizes a high field superconductor?

High field superconductors are characterized by the fact that the critical magnetic field is so high, that the effect of the field on the electron spins as well as on the electron orbits has to be taken into account.

The interaction Hamiltonian is then given by $H_{int} = H_{int}^{(1)} + H_{int}^{(2)}$ where

$$H_{int}^{(1)} = - \frac{e}{mc} \, A.p \quad \text{(effect of field on orbits)}$$

$$(1)$$

$$H_{int}^{(2)} = - \mu_B \, H \sum \sigma_Z^{(i)} \text{(effect of field on spins)}$$

The summation index i refers to different electrons. A thumb rule argument tells us that if we are dealing with a probe which has a critical field of the order $H_c \simeq 18.6 \, T_c$ KG, where the transition temperature T_c is measured in degrees, than the effect

of the field on the electron spins is important and has
to be considered. (Clogston criterium).[1]

2. How to obtain high field superconductors?

There are essentially two ways to produce high
field superconductors. One way consists in finding
materials with very high Ginzburg-Landau   - parameters such as Ti-V and Nb- Zr alloys first investigated
by Berlincourt and Hake[2], (see also Ref. (3)).

The other way consists in producing very thin and
very dirty films such as the 100Å Al films investigated
by Strongin et al.[4] with a mean free path of a few
Angstroms. If set into a parallel field such films can
sustain extremely high fields.

3. What are the special features of high field super-
conductors?

High field superconductors can show first order
phase transitions to the normal state if the temperature is low enough[5] and if there is not too much spin-
orbital scattering. [6]

Such first order phase transitions have not yet
been detected experimentally but there seems little
doubt that they will be eventually seen.

4. Outline of the lecture.

In order to obtain an understanding of the case of
a field acting on spin and orbit of the electrons, we
will first study the two cases separately and later
combine the results. Furthermore we will consider
first the case of zero temperature and no spin-orbital

scattering but later assume finite values for both quantities.

II. THEORY OF HIGH FIELD SUPERCONDUCTORS

1. Zero temperature limit and absence of spin-orbital scattering.

a) Field acting on electron spins only.

We consider the case of zero temperature and no spin-orbital scattering. Then the free energy of the normal state as function of field is given by

$$F \ (H) = F \ (0) - \frac{\chi}{2} H^2 \qquad (2)$$

where $\chi = 2\mu_B^2 \ N(0)$ is the Pauli spin-susceptibility. Thus for $\mu H = \Delta_0 / 2$ the energy of the normal state will be equal to the BCS condensation energy $-N(0)/2 \ \Delta_0^2$ (see Fig. (1)). Hereby Δ_0 is the order parameter in the absence of the field. The excitation spectrum for spin up and down electrons in the superconductor is given by

$$E_\uparrow (p) = (\epsilon p^2 + \Delta^2)^{1/2} + \mu H \qquad (3)$$

$$E_\downarrow (p) = (\epsilon p^2 + \Delta^2)^{1/2} - \mu H$$

where $\epsilon \rho = V_F (p - p_F)$.

For $h = \mu_B H / \Delta < 1$ we find $E_\downarrow, E_\uparrow > 0$ and it will be energetically disadvantageous to break up Cooper pairs since the gain in energy due to spin alignment is smaller than the loss of pairing energy.

Thus the superconductor will not respond to the field and the free energy will be independent of field in that region (see Fig. 1). However it turns out (see Ref. (5)) that for $\frac{1}{2} < h < 1$ there is another manifold of states with a free energy shown in Fig. (1) by a dashed line, with the property that those states are stable against small changes in the configuration. For a given value of h such a state has unpaired electrons of spin down occupying a shell around the Fermi level (Fig. (2)). The unpaired electrons block the momentum states which they occupy for virtual pair scattering. Those states have thus to be excluded from the effective scattering volume in momentum space which appears in the equation for the order parameter, leading to a reduction of the latter. The determining equation for the order parameter is now of the form

$$\frac{1}{V} = \sum_{\substack{p, \text{ excl.} \\ \text{shell}}} 2^{-1}(6p^2 + \Delta^2)^{-1/2} \qquad (4)$$

where V is the BCS electron interaction constant. The thickness of the shell is determined by the condition that on the surface of the shell $E_{\downarrow} = 0$.

Together with Eq. (4) this determines the order parameter Δ self consistently. Fig. (3) shows Δ/Δ_0 as function of h. In the region $1/2 < h < 1$ we have the two solutions corresponding to a completely paired and a partially unpaired state.

b) Field acting on electron orbits only.

In order to obtain a qualitative understanding of the effect of the field acting on the electron orbits we

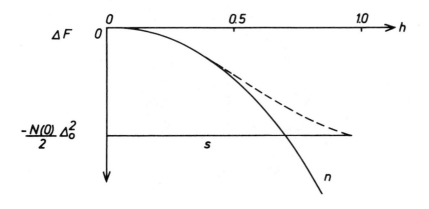

Fig. 1. Change in free energy ΔF vs. magnetic field $h = \mu_B H/\Delta_o$. The dashed line indicates another manifold of states which can exist for $1/2 < h < 1$.

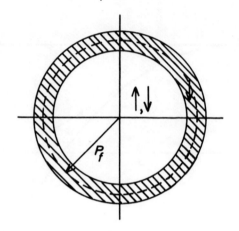

Fig. 2. Shaded region is shell of unpaired electrons around the Fermi level which occur in
states corresponding to dashed line in Fig. 1.

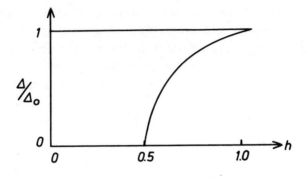

Fig. 3.   The order parameter Δ plotted as a function of h.

restrict ourselves to thin films with thickness d much smaller than the penetration depth. We will study first another situation which will turn out to be closely related to the above one, namely that of the uniform current flowing through the film.

Furthermore let us assume first that the mean free path $l \rightarrow \infty$ so that momentum is a good quantum number. Than by applying an electric field for a short period of time a current is induced and the electron distribution in momentum space is shifted by a vector $\mathbf{q}$ and looks like shown in Fig. (4).

The excitation spectrum of the quasiparticles is then given by

$$Ep = (\epsilon_p^2 + \Delta^2)^{1/2} + \mathbf{q}\,\mathbf{p}/m$$
$$= (\epsilon_p^2 + \Delta^2)^{1/2} + qv_F \cos \qquad (5)$$

where $\mathbf{p}$ is measured in the rest frame of the Cooper pairs. It is seen that for $q > q_S = V_F/\Delta_0$, Ep can become negative which means that it is energetically favourable for some of the Cooper pairs to break up. This implies that the system becomes gapless (see Fig. 5). The region of unpaired electrons in momentum space is blocked for virtual pair scattering and leads to a reduction of the order parameter similarly as found above for the field acting on the electron spins only (see Eq. (4)). The order parameter as function of $S = q/q_S$ is shown in Fig. (6). If we want to treat the case of finite mean free path we have to apply a more powerful method than the one used here since momentum is then no longer a good quantum number and no pictures may be be drawn any longer in momentum space. Such a method is the Green's function method which can be used for

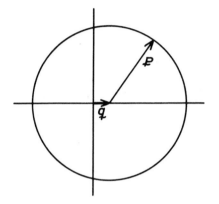

Fig. 4. The electron distribution in momentum
space when a current flows (under ideal
conditions).

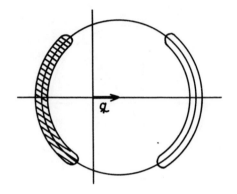

Fig. 5. For $q > q_s = \nu_F/\Delta_0$, E_p can become
negative; it is then energetically favourable for
some of the Cooper pairs to break up.

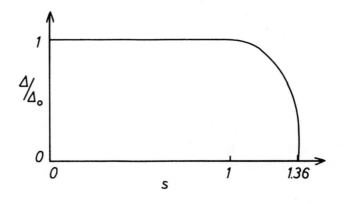

Fig. 6. The order parameter Δ as a function
of $s = q/q_s$ $(1 \rightarrow \infty)$.

arbitary mean free paths and which was applied in this
context first by Maki.[1] The results are especially
simple in the dirty limit where $1 \ll \xi_0$ and ξ_0 is the coherence distance.

It turns out that the order parameter is decreasing
even for small values of q but otherwise behaves qualitatively the same way as in the clean case if s is set
equal to

$$s = \frac{2}{3} \frac{\tau v_F^2 q^2}{\Delta_0}$$

where $\tau = 1/v_F$ (see Fig. (7)).

In order to establish the connection to the situation
of an applied field parallel to the film acting on the
electron orbits only, we just have to replace

$$q^2 \rightarrow e^2 <A^2 (x)> = e^2 d^2 H^2 /12$$

where the brackets indicate a spatial average over the
sample. This was proved first by Maki[8] and seems
intuitively plausible if one thinks of the effect of the
field as inducing a screening current.

c) Combination of both effects.

In order to understand the combined effect of a
field acting on the spins as well as on the orbits of the
electrons we draw the contours of Δ = const in the
h vs. s plane[9] first assuming h and s to be independent
quantities. The result is shown in Fig. (8). Along the
axis s = 0 we recover the results shown in Fig. (3)
while along the axis h = 0 we obtain back again the results shown in Fig. (7). It is seen from Fig. (8) how
the region with two solutions for $\Delta(h)$ which was
closely connected with the occurance of a first order
phase transition penetrates from the s = 0 axis into the
h vs. s plane.

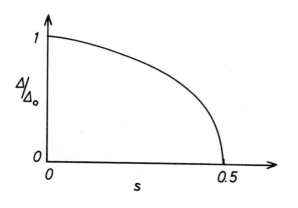

Fig. 7. The order parameter Δ as a function
of s in the dirty limit $1 \ll \xi_0$

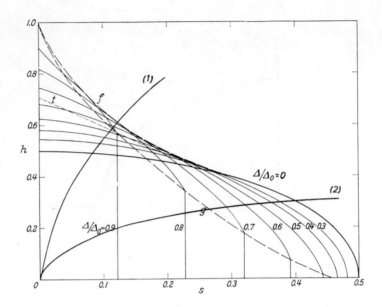

Fig. 8. Contours of Δ -- constant in the h vs. s plane.

The folding line "f" indicates where the first sheet of solution goes over into the second sheet. The line "t" indicates those states in the first sheet which have a free energy which is equal to the one in the normal state. This implies that along the t-line a first order phase transition will occur if there is no superheating or super-cooling. Since $h \sim H$ and $s \sim H^2$ the quantities h and s are not independent of each other for a given thin film sample. Instead they are connected by the relationship

$$s = ch^2 \qquad (6)$$

where $c = \tau v_F^2 e^2 d^2 \Delta_0 / 18 \mu_B^2$ is determined by the properties of the film under consideration. In Fig. (8) we have drawn Eq. (6) for two different films. The following features may be read off immediately. If the film is thin and dirty enough so that $c < 1.66$ the corresponding parabola such as the one labeled (1) in Fig. (8) will intersect the t - and f - line and the $\Delta = 0$ line at fields h_t, h_f, h_Δ respectively. We can interpret those three fields as (a) the field at which the free energies of superconducting and normal state become equal, (b) the superheating field above which the film can not stay superconducting, (c) the supercooling field. On the other hand if the film is such that $c > 1.66$ then the corresponding parabola (see for example the one labeled (2) in Fig. (8)) will not intersect the t- and f-line but the $\Delta = 0$ line only. The phase transition from the super-conducting to the normal state is then always of second order.[10]

2. Extension to finite temperatures ($T \neq 0$)

In order to understand the changes caused by finite temperature we consider again the two separate cases of a field acting on the electron spins and on the electron orbits. Let us first investigate the case of a field acting on the spins only. Since the quasiparticles in a superconductor created by thermal excitation can line up their spins with respect to the field, a finite temperature will lead to a non-vanishing spin-susceptibility of the superconducting state. Thus we expect that the phase transition to the normal state will be of second order if the temperature and thus the spin-susceptibility in the superconductor are high enough. Consequently the order parameter $\Delta(h)/\Delta_0$ should become a single valued function for large enough values of $t = T/T_{co}$ where T_{co} is the transition temperature of the sample in the absence of any field.

This is born out indeed by the numerical calculations done in Ref. (5) which we show schematically in Fig. (9). If we consider the case of a field acting on the electron orbits only, we don't expect any peculiarities. In Fig. (10) it is indicated how $\Delta(s)/\Delta_0$ changes for different values of $t = T/T_{co}$. If we combine both pictures we obtain Fig. (11) where the contours of vanishing order parameter $\Delta(t) = 0$ have been drawn for different reduced temperatures t together with the corresponding folding lines "f." It is seen that the region with two solutions for the order parameter, vanishes for $t > 0.56$.

For a given film we can read of immediately the critical field $h_c(t)$ by drawing the corresponding parabola and looking at the intersections of this parabola with the $\Delta(t) = 0$ lines.

Fig. (10) shows furthermore that for small values of t the $\Delta(t) = 0$ lines across the $\Delta(t = 0) = 0$ line. A quantitative calculation shows that this cross over occurs for $h > s$ depending on the temperature t. This

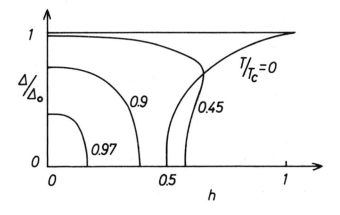

Fig. 9. Numerical results for Δ vs. h at finite temperatures.

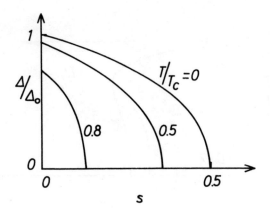

Fig. 10. Δ vs s at finite temperatures.

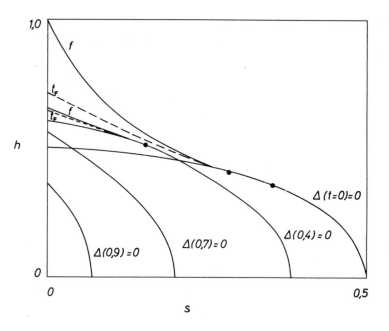

Fig. 11. Contours of $\Delta(t) = 0$ in the h vs. s plane.

can lead to peculiar effects if the films are such that
the corresponding c values lie in the range $2.86 > c$
$> 1.66.$ If those films are brought into a parallel
magnetic field which is such that at $t = 0$ the film is
just normal, then because of the cross over of the
$\Delta(t) = 0$ line the order parameter as function of temperature may look like shown in Fig. (12). This implies that the film which is normal at $T = 0$ becomes
superconducting at a temperature T_1 before it becomes
normal again at a higher temperature T_2. However it
turns out that this effect is rather sensitive to spin-
orbital mean free path. For this reason we don't think
that it has any practical bearings but have mentioned it
for curiosity only.

3. Effects of spin-orbital mean free path.

The effect of spin orbital scattering is understood
most easily by first considering again the two situations
of a field acting on the spins and on the electron orbits
separately. Let us restrict ourselves first to $T = 0$
and consider the case of a field acting on the spins only.
From the theory of the Knight-shift in superconductors
we know that in the presence of spin-orbital scattering
the spin susceptibility is non vanishing even for $T = 0.$
The physical reason for this to occur is that the
electrons are no longer paired in spin up and down
states but rather in more general time reversed spin
states. Such a pairing however allows for response to
an applied magnetic field thus leading to a finite spin
susceptibility. For this reason we expect that for
strong enough spin-orbital scattering the phase transition to the normal state will be always of second order
similarly as it was found to be the case for high enough

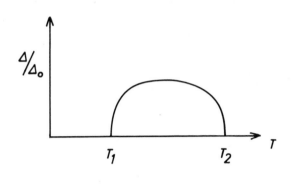

Fig. 12. Theoretical variation of Δ with T for films in parallel magnetic field, if at T = 0 film is just normal.

temperatures where a finite spin susceptibility resulted from the thermal excitations. In Fig. (13) we
show schematically the behavior of $\Delta(h)/\Delta_0$ for $T = 0$
and different values of the spin-orbital scattering rate
$1/\tau_{so}$.[11] Such a rate is introduced conveniently into
the theory by assuming random scattering centers with
a scattering potential $V(p - p')$ containing a time reversal invariant spin-flip term. We write

$$V(p,p') = V_1(p - p') + \frac{i\, v_{so}}{p_F^2} [p \times p']\sigma \qquad (7)$$

Then τ_{so}^{-1} is given by

$$\frac{1}{\tau_{so}} = n_i \frac{N(0)}{2} \int d\Omega\, v_{so}^2 \sin\theta \qquad (8)$$

where n_i is the concentration of the scattering centers.
Numerical calculations show that for $1/\tau_{so}\Delta_0 > 6.96$,
$\Delta(h)/\Delta_0$ is a single valued function of h. As far as the
effect of the field on the electron orbits is concerned,
spin-orbital scattering does not have any influence and
$\Delta(s)/\Delta_0$ is uneffected by $1/\tau_{so}\Delta_0$. If we add again both
pictures then for fixed value of $1/\tau_{so}\Delta_0$ the contours of
$\Delta(t) = 0$ look like indicated in Fig. (14). We have not
indicated the folding lines "f" in this plot since they are
difficult to calculate for this general case. For a given
film one can read off the critical field $h_c(t)$ immediately by drawing the corresponding parabola and looking
at the intersections with the $\Delta(t) = 0$ lines. One can try
to determine this way the quantities c and $1/\tau_{so}\Delta_0$ appropriate for the 100Å thick Al films produced by
Strongin et al. for which $h_c(t)$ was measured.[11] Good
quantitative agreement with the measurements (see

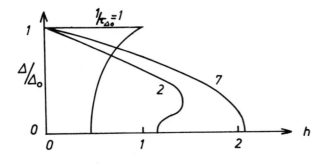

Fig. 13. Schematic behavior of Δ vs. h (at
T = 0) for different values of the spin-orbital
scattering rate $1/\tau_{so}$.

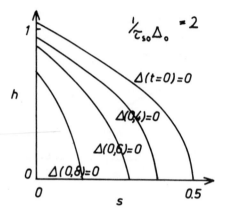

Fig. 14. $\Delta = 0$ contours at different temperatures for fixed scattering rates $1/\tau_{so}$ in the h vs. s plane.

Fig. (15)) is obtained by choosing $c \simeq 0.1$ and
$1/\tau_{s0}\Delta_0 \simeq 1$.

It should be noted that spin-orbital scattering is
not strong enough in these films to prevent first order
phase transitions at low enough temperatures ($t < 0.4$).
The mean free path calculated from the value of $c \simeq 0.1$
turns out to be only a few Ångströms. This may raise
some objections as to the validity of the theory used for
the quantitive calculations since latter always assumes
that $p_F l \gg 1$. If this assumption is not made the standard diagramatic method for dealing with randomly distributed scattering centers can not be used.

4. Extension to type II superconductors.

Many of the results obtained before for the thin
film case may be used also for type II high field superconductors if we work in the dirty limit ($l \ll \xi_0$). It
turns out that there is a certain equivalence if we consider the pair-breaking effect of the magnetic field on
the electron orbits for a thin film and a type II sample.[12]
The equivalence is limited to the computation of quantities which can be obtained from the linear term of the
generalized Ginzburg-Landau equation. It states that
those quantities are the same for a thin film and a type
II superconductor if the quantity $s = \tau v_F^2 e^2 d^2 H^2/18\Delta_0$
for the thin film is replaced by

$$s = \tau v_F^2 eH/6\Delta_0$$

for the type II case. Thus all calculations of contours
of $\Delta(t) = 0$ apply for the type II situation. The same is
not true for the folding line "f" and the t-line for example, since those quantities can not be obtained from

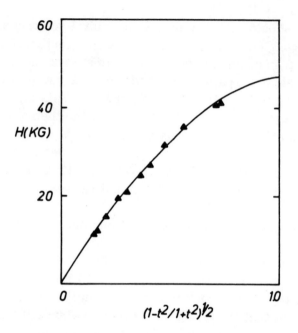

Fig. 15. Theoretical and experimental results for H_c as a function of τ (with c $\cong 0.1$ and

$$\frac{1}{\tau_{so}\Delta_0} \simeq 1)$$

the linearized Ginzburg-Landau equation. If one wants
to calculate the critical field for a type II high field
superconductors one first has to realize that there exists now a linear relationship between s and h of the
form

$$s = \alpha h \qquad (9)$$

where $\alpha = 3\mu_B/c\tau v_F^2$ is the so called Maki-parameter.
For a given sample α is fixed. Instead of drawing a
parabola in the (s, h) plane as it was done for the thin
films we now draw a straight line given by Eq. (9).
The intersections with the $\Delta(t) = 0$ lines (see Figs.
(11), (14)) give the critical field $h_{c2}(t)$. It is identical
with the one calculated in Refs. (13) and (14). If α
is small enough and t and $1/\tau_{so}$ are not too large it
should be kept in mind that the field determined this
way is the supercooling field.

REFERENCES

1. A. M. Clogston Phys. Rev. Letters 9, 266 (1962).
   B. S. Chandrasekhar Appl. Phys. Letters 1,
   7 (1962).

2. T. G. Berlincourt and R. R. Hake, Phys. Rev. 131,
   140, (1963).

3. E. J. Saur, Lecture held at the Advanced Summer
   Study Institute on Superconductivity, McGill
   University, Montreal, 1968.

4. M. Strongin and O. F. Kammerer, Phys. Rev.
   Letters 16, 456 (1966).

5. G. J. Sarma, Jorn. Phys. Chem. Solids 24, 1029 (1963).

6. K. Maki and T. Tsuneto, Progr. Theor. Phys. (Kyoto) 31, 945 (1964). H. Engler and P. Fulde, Phys. kond. Materie 7, 150 (1968).

7. K. Maki, Progr. Theor. Phys. (Kyoto) 29, 10 and 333 (1963).

8. K. Maki, Progr. Theor. Phys. (Kyoto) 31, 731 (1964).

9. R. Avenhaus and P. Fulde, Phys. kond. Materie 5, 157 (1966).

10. K. Maki, Progr. Theor. Phys. (Kyoto) 32, 29 (1964).

11. R. Avenhaus, doctoral thesis, TH Karlsruhe (1967).

12. K. Maki, Physics 1, 127.

13. N. R. Werthamer, E. Helfand, and P. Hohenberg, Phys. Rev. 147, 295 (1966).

14. K. Maki, Phys. Rev. 148, 362 (1966).

PROXIMITY EFFECTS
OF THICK SUPERCONDUCTING FILM

P. Fulde

Institut für Theoretische Physik
Universität Frankfurt/Main

I. INTRODUCTION

The proximity effect, that is the mutual influence of superconducting and normal films being in metallic contact, has been studied extensively, both theoretically as well as experimentally.[1] For example it has been found that the transition temperature of such a contact will be a function of the two films thicknesses involved and that it can vary continuously from the transition temperature of one film to the one of the other film. Since Cooper-pairs as well as unpaired electrons will drift from one film into the other such a contact will generally lead to a space dependent orderparameter $\Delta(r)$. De Gennes and Guyon[1] have shown how the mutual influence of two films which are in contact can be described by proper boundary conditions for $\Delta(r)$ at the interface and at the metal-vacuum boundary. The situation is especially simple, if the superconducting film is in contact with a magnetic film, such as Fe, Ni, Co.

565

Because of the strong pair breaking effect exerted by magnetic atoms on the Cooper-pairs the order parameter approaches zero at the metallic interface[2] (see Fig. 1).

In the following we will restrict ourselves to just this situation. Our aim will be to calculate thermodynamical quantities such as the jump in the specific heat at T_c for thick superconducting films in metallic contact with paramagnetic films.[3] It will turn out that the jump in the specific heat is a much more sensitive measure of the proximity effect than is the reduction in transition temperature for example. Thus there may be still an appreciable reduction of the jump in the specific heat for superconducting films which are so thick that no change in the transition temperature should be observable.

An essential advantage in doing the calculations for a thick superconducting film in metallic contact is that the non-linear Ginzburg-Landau equation can be solved exactly. This provides a tool for calculating not only the jump in the specific heat at T_c but also the specific heat in the vicinity of T_c without doing any approximation. This will turn out to be important since the specific heat below T_c is not a monotonic function of temperature as the superconducting film becomes thick enough.

II. THERMODYNAMICAL PROPERTIES

In calculating the spatial variation of the order parameter $\Delta(\mathbf{r})$ for the contact under consideration we may use the ordinary rather than the generalized Ginzburg-Landau equation since the effect of the

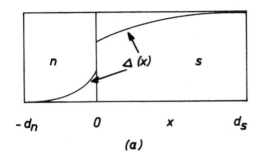

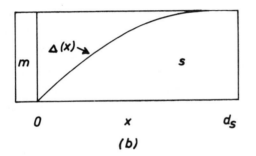

Fig. 1. Variation of order parameter near metallic interface a) between normal (nonmagnetic) and superconducting metals b) between magnetic film and superconductor.

contact on the transition temperature is very small.
If we assume furthermore that we are in the clean
limit $l \gg \xi_0$ where l is the mean free and ξ_0 is the
coherence length then $\Delta (\mathbf{r})$ is determined by

$$(\ln T/T_{cs} - \frac{\pi^2}{4} \xi^2 \nabla_r^2) \Delta (\mathbf{r}) + \frac{7\zeta(3)}{8(\pi T)^2} |\Delta(\mathbf{r})|^2 \Delta(\mathbf{r}) = 0 \qquad (1)$$

Hereby is T_{cs} the transition temperature in the absence of the contact and $\xi(T) = v_F/2\pi T$. The boundary
conditions for the order parameter can be written
as (see Fig. 1b)

$$\Delta(0) = 0, \quad \frac{d\Delta}{dx}\bigg|_{x=ds} = 0 \qquad (2)$$

At the transition temperature $\Delta(\mathbf{r})$ becomes arbitrarily
small so that the second term in Eq. (1) can be dropped.
This implies that at T_c, $\Delta(x)$ is an eigenfunction of ∇_x^2.
With the boundary conditions (2) this leads to

$$\Delta(x) \sim \sin \frac{\pi}{2ds} x \qquad (3)$$

at the transition. However as we depart from T_c we
expect the non-linear part of Eq. (1) to become in-
creasingly important as the films become thicker and
thicker. This can be seen in detail by studying the
solutions of the non-linear Eq. (1). It is know that the
Jacobi doubly periodic functions[4]

$$\varphi = \varphi_0 \, sn(qx + c, k) \qquad (4)$$

satisfy the differential equation

$$-\frac{\varphi_0^2}{2k^2q^2}\frac{d^2}{dx^2}\varphi - \varphi_0^2\frac{(1+k^2)}{2k^2}\varphi + \varphi^3 = 0 \tag{5}$$

The function sn (x, k) has the following limiting properties

$$sn(x, k) = \begin{cases} \sin x, & k = 0 \\ \tanh x, & k = 1 \end{cases} \tag{6}$$

Since Eq. (5) is of the type of Eq. (1) we try the following ansatz for $\Delta(x)$

$$\Delta(x) = \Delta_0 \, sn \, (qx + c, k) \tag{7}$$

By comparing Eqs. (1) and (5) we obtain

$$\Delta_0^2 = \frac{8(\pi T)^2}{7\zeta(3)} \ln \frac{T_{cs}}{T} \frac{2k^2}{1 + k^2}$$

$$(1 + k^2)q^2 = \frac{4}{\pi^2\xi^2} \ln \frac{T_{cs}}{T} \tag{8}$$

The boundary conditions (2) can be satisfied by setting

$$c = 0, \quad q = \frac{K(k^2)}{d_s} \tag{9}$$

where $K(k^2)$ is the well known complete elliptic integral.[4] From Eqs. (3) and (6) it is clear that $k = 0$ for $T = T_c$. This enables us to re-write the second of Eqs. (8) as

$$(1 + k^2)\left(\frac{2}{\pi}K(k^2)\right)^2 = \frac{T^2\ln(T_{cs}/T)}{T_c^2 \ln(T_{cs}/T)} \tag{10}$$

With the help of the last equation we can calculate k^2 as function of T/T_{cs} for given values of T_c which in turn is determined by the properties of film and can be computed from the linearized Eq. (1). Numerical results are shown in Fig. (2). One notices that k^2 as function of T/T_{cs} changes near T_c the faster the larger the ratio T_c/T_{cs} is, that is the thicker the films are. A change of k^2 however implies a change of the spatial dependence of $\Delta(x)$. This can be seen in detail from Fig. (3) where

$$\text{sn } K(k^2) \; x/d_s$$

is plotted <u>vs.</u> x/d_s for different values of k^2.[4]

Figures (2) and (3) give a complete picture of the spatial variation of $\Delta(x)$ for different film thicknesses.

Equation (7) can be used to derive an analytic expression for the difference Δc in the specific heat between superconducting and normal state of the contacts under consideration. One starts out with the free energy expression

$$\Delta F = - \frac{N(0)}{2} \frac{7\zeta(3)}{8(\pi T)^2} \langle \Delta^4(\mathbf{r}) \rangle \qquad (11)$$

and computes from this the entropy and the specific heat. If we introduce the normalized function

$$\Delta c = 7\zeta(3) \; (4m \; p_F T_{cs})^{-1} \; \Delta c$$

we obtain after some calculations[3]

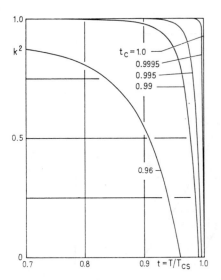

Fig. 2. Numerical solutions of eq. (10) for k^2 vs. T/T_{cs}.

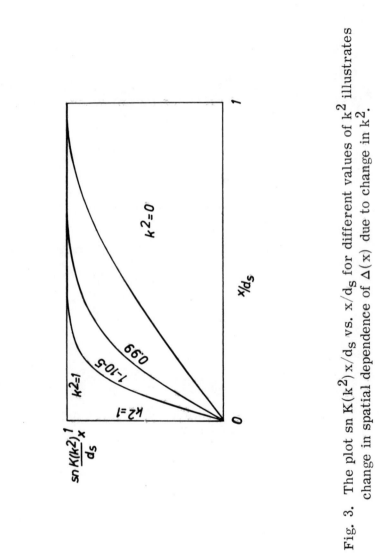

Fig. 3. The plot sn $K(k^2)\, x/d_s$ vs. x/d_s for different values of k^2 illustrates change in spatial dependence of $\Delta(x)$ due to change in k^2.

$$\Delta c = \frac{T}{T_{cs}} \left\{ (2\ln \frac{T_{cs}}{T} - 1)^2 \frac{(1 - E/K)^2 - k^2}{1 - E/K - k^2(1 + E/K)} \right.$$

$$+ \frac{2}{1 + k^2} (1 - \frac{E}{K}) \ln \frac{T_{cs}}{T} (1 - 2 \ln \frac{T_{cs}}{T})$$

$$\left. - \frac{4k^2}{(1 + k^2)^2} (\ln \frac{T_{cs}}{T})^2 \right\} \qquad (12)$$

Hereby is $E(k^2)$ the well known elliptic integral. Equation (12) can be used together with Fig. (2) to calculate the specific heat in the neighborhood of T_c. Numerical results are shown in Fig. (4). The interesting point to notice is that even for very thick films (such as $a/\xi(T_c) = 60$) the reduction in the jump of the specific heat as compared with the one in the absence of the contact is still appreciable. However the transition temperature of such films would be hardly changed by the contact ($t_c = 0.9995$). The sensitivity of the specific heat to proximity effects is related to the spatial variation of the order parameter which can be characterized by the quantity

$$\beta = \langle \Delta^4(\mathbf{r}) \rangle / \langle \Delta^2(\mathbf{r}) \rangle^2$$

At T_c we find with the help of Eq. (3) that $\beta = 3/2$. As a consequence for $(T_{cs} - T_c) \ll T_{cs}$ the jump in the specific heat at T_c becomes close to $\Delta c = 1/\beta$ or $\Delta c = 2/3$. From Fig. (4) it becomes apparent how the BCS limit is approached if the superconducting film becomes infinitely thick.

The above considerations can be extended in two ways. We can include the effect of mean free path,

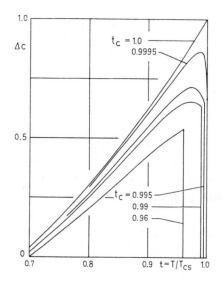

Fig. 4. Numerical results for the difference in specific heat between superconducting and normal states, Δc, vs. T/T_{cs} in the neighbourhood of T_c.

and we can relax the condition $\Delta(0) = 0$ to allow for general contacts as indicated in Fig. (1a). With these two generalizations of the theory one can make an attempt to explain the reductions in Δc found by Shiffman et al[5] for eutectic Pb-Su alloys.

One difficulty however in making such a comparison is the fact that the mean free path in the eutectic material was not determined to the required accuracy. If we use the available datas by Shiffman et al we find for the jump in the specific heat at T_c, $\Delta c_{thcor} = 0.70$ while the experimental value is $\Delta c_{exp} = 0.78$. Regarding the fact that the calculations depend rather sensitively on mean free path the agreement between the theoretical and the experimental value can be regarded as reasonable.

REFERENCES

1. P. G. de Gennes and E. Guyon, Physics letters 3, 168 (1963). G. Deutscher and P. G. de Gennes: Proximity Effects; to be published in Superconductivity, edited by R. Parks; New York, Marcel Dekker Publ. (in print). This extensive review article contains all references to the subject.

2. W. Silvert has raised some objections concerning this simple boundary condition (private communication).

3. P. Fulde and W. Moormann, Phy. kondens. Materie 6, 403 (1967).

4. Jahnke-Emde-Lösch, Tafeln höherer Funktionen, Stuttgart, B. G. Teubner, 1960.

5. C. A. Shiffman, J. F. Cochran and M. Garber
   Rev. Mod. Phys. 36, 127 (1964).

SUPERCONDUCTIVITY
AND
THE KONDO EFFECT

A. Griffin

SUPERCONDUCTIVITY
AND
THE KONDO EFFECT

A. Griffin
Department of Physics
University of Toronto
Toronto, Ontario, Canada

I. INTRODUCTION

Eight years ago, Abrikosov and Gor'kov[1] gave
a very successful theory of the effect of random, un-
polarized magnetic impurities on superconductivity.
As is well known, this theory has been amazingly
accurate. One of the novel implications was the prediction of "gapless" superconductivity-that is, the
magnetic impurities not only weakened Cooper pair
formation, but actually changed the qualitative
nature of the condensate. Maki has recently given
a review[2] of the properties of gapless superconductors, to which we refer the reader. From a certain
point of view, the depression in the transition temperature T_c of a superconductor caused by magnetic
impurities is especially important. At the present
time, it is commonly used as a sort of diagnostic
tool in studying the nature of impurities-if T_c is
strongly depressed, then in some sense, the impurity is thought to have a "magnetic moment".

According to the AG theory, the initial decrease in T_c is given by

$$\Delta T_c \simeq \pi/4\tau_s, \qquad (1)$$

where τ_s is the electronic lifetime due to exchange scattering (We set $\hbar = k_B = 1$ throughout these lectures). In Born approximation, we have

$$\frac{1}{\tau_s} = 2\pi(\frac{N_i}{N})\frac{N(o)}{N} \langle \mathbf{S} \cdot \mathbf{S} \rangle (\frac{J}{2})^2, \qquad (2)$$

where N_i is the number of impurities, N is the number of atoms in the host crystal (of unit volume) and $N(o)$ is the usual density of states at the Fermi surface. The expression in Eq. (1) is often fitted (see, for example, Refs. 3 and 4) to experimental results in order to obtain estimates of the exchange constant J and the impurity spin magnitude S. It is clearly of great interest to see what happens if the AG theory is generalized. In particular, is the depression in T_c always simply related to the effective impurity magnetic moment in the normal state?

The AG theory is restricted in several ways:

(1) The jth impurity is assumed to be described by a well defined spin vector $\hat{\mathbf{S}}^j$, which is coupled to the conduction electron spin density $\hat{\mathbf{s}}(r)$ by an exchange interaction of the form

$$\hat{H}_{sd} = -\frac{1}{N} \sum_{j=1}^{N_i} \int d\mathbf{r}\, J(\mathbf{r} - \mathbf{R}_j)\hat{\mathbf{S}}^j \cdot \hat{\mathbf{s}}(r). \qquad (3)$$

In this connection, we note that the exchange interaction is usually assumed to be very localized near the impurity, and thus to a good approximation, we

have $J(\mathbf{r}) = J\delta(\mathbf{r})$. This is more accurate for rare
earth atoms, where the impurity spin arises from
empty f-electron orbitals, than it is for transition
element atoms with missing d-electrons. In general,
one has $J_{sf} > 0$ (ferromagnetic coupling); $J_{sd} < 0$
(antiferromagnetic coupling). As we shall see, the
consequences of the Kondo effect are much more
dramatic for the latter case. Let us note here that
while the use of a delta function exchange interaction
may give rise to some artificial divergences for
high momentum values, this is no real problem
since a cutoff at $k_c \sim k_F$ may always be introduced
in a natural manner. The crucial restriction implicit in (3) is simply that a well defined spin **S**
exists.

(2) All effects of the impurity spin dynamics
are neglected. The impurity spin **S** is a quantum
mechanical operator and has $2S + 1$ possible orien-
tations relative to some axis of quantization. Thus
it is quite different from an impurity potential, which
is essentially an external field. Formally, this
means AG treated the components of **S** as commuting
operators, when in truth they obey angular momentum commutation relations

$$[\hat{S}_x, \hat{S}_y] = i\hat{S}_z, \qquad (4)$$

and cyclic permutations thereof. We might recall
here that the strong destructive effect of impurity
spins on superconductivity is usually understood to
arise because (3) is a time-reversal breaking perturbation.[2] That is, $\hat{S}_z$ is the analogue of a magnetic
field and acts differently on the electrons in the time-
reversed states which form Cooper pairs. This

analogy becomes more tenuous when one treats the impurity as an angular momentum operator.

(3) AG treated the exchange scattering in lowest order of perturbation theory - i.e., the electronic cross section was proportional to J^2.

(4) Finally the effective Rudermann-Kittel-Kasuya-Yosida interaction [which is induced between different impurity spins by the conduction electrons acting via the exchange interaction] is not considered. This was later included by Gor'kov and Rusinov[5], in so far as it is described by a constant exchange field I_z which is computed self-consistently. This is still within the spirit of AG in treating S like an external field. In his lectures at this summer school, Dr. Bennemann has reviewed Gor'kov and Rusinov's static molecular field theory and has worked out the consequences of a plausible generalization which includes the dynamical effects of the RKKY interaction. To do this rigorously is difficult since the dynamical effects are tied up with the angular momentum commutation relations.

The preceding restrictions are obviously related to each other. In fact, they are all different aspects of the so-called "Kondo problem" or "Kondo effect". By the Kondo effect, I mean the consequences of two facts:

(a) S is a dynamical variable (but neither a fermion or boson).

(b) Conduction electrons obey Fermi statistics and hence there is a well defined Fermi surface. More precisely, the Pauli exclusion principle must be carefully taken into account when one considers the intermediate states in electron scattering from an impurity.

Since Kondo's original paper in 1964 on the resistance minimum of dilute alloys, the Kondo problem has been in a rapid state of development and it will probably continue to play a central role in the study of the low temperature properties of metals for several more years (for a readable introduction, see Ref. 6). Within the last half year, there has been great progress in understanding the precise mathematical implications of several theories. However, the validity of all current discussions is still somewhat controversial, as we shall see. As a word of warning, I might note that experimental results are often quoted as giving definitive proof of one theoretical picture when in truth, they can be understood equally well by another theory. In these lectures, I shall assume that the correct theory for multiple scattering of an electron by an impurity spin is that associated with the names Suhl[7], Abrikosov[8] and Nagaoka.[9] The mathematical equivalence of the work of these three authors (who used quite different approaches) has been proven by many people (see Refs. 10 and 11 for further details and earlier references). In turn, exact solutions are available for the S.A.N. integral equations.[7,12,13] The appropriate generalization of the Suhl-Abrikosov form of the scattering equations has been written down by Maki[14] for the case of a superconductor. Zuckermann[15] has very recently done the same using the Nagaoka approach. Some alternatives to the S.A.N. theory will be briefly noted for completeness.

Let me say immediately that I will not discuss restriction (1), that is, the conditions under which the localized electrons associated with an impurity produce a well defined spin **S**. One theory of this is based on Anderson's Hamiltonian, which predicts one has a net spin if the coulomb repulsion (U) between two d-electrons is large enough and the coupling between the conduction electrons and the d-electrons (V) is weak enough. This type of study is, of course, a more basic approach and detailed studies[16] show that Kondo-type divergencies arise in the Anderson Hamiltonian as well. Several studies [for references, see Zuckermann[17]] have been made of this Hamiltonian including, in addition, a B.C.S. attractive interaction between the conduction electrons. However, these calculations have been limited to the first Born approximation and thus do not pick up intrinsic Kondo effects. Schrieffer and Woolf[18] have pointed out that a canonical transformation on the Anderson Hamiltonian gives rise to an effective interaction of the form (3), with an antiferromagnetic exchange constant

$$\frac{J}{2N} \cong \frac{-V^2 U}{E_d(E_d + U)} \tag{5}$$

where E_d is the energy of the d-electron below the Fermi energy ϵ_F. The same transformation may lead to an additional repulsive interaction between the conduction electrons in the case of superconductors.[19] More careful studies would be useful in this area, with the goal of understanding the relation of Kondo divergences and localized spin fluctuations (paramagnons) resulting from the repeated scattering between electrons and holes of opposite spin.

I shall also neglect the RKKY interaction between impurities. The Kondo effect will occur even

for one impurity spin in a free electron gas. However, even if a small concentration of random impurities are treated as independent scatterers,
they may give rise to a net effect on the conduction
electrons as they propagate between different impurities. In terms of graphical language, this kind
of "medium effect" is naturally included by computing
self-energy diagrams self-consistently with the true
Green's function, rather than the bare propagator.
In almost all calculations of the Kondo effect in
dilute alloys in the normal state, this renormalization effect directly shows up in the bulk electronic
density of states $\rho(\omega)$ [such as measured in tunneling measurements]. Thus the predicted[12, 13]
anomalies in the specific heat of dilute alloys
[which is determined completely by $\rho(\omega)$] are tan-
tamount to saying that the SAN scattering equations
must be reformulated so as to involve the self-
consistent density of states. To say the least, this
complicates things considerably. Nagaoka[20] tried
to make this generalization of his theory. Perhaps
the unphysical conclusions he drew were a result
of his using an incorrect solution[9] for the one impurity case.

The importance of treating the renormalization effect of many independent impurities is clearly
very important in the case of superconductors, even
if it turns out to not be so essential for normal
metals. Thus perhaps the anomaly in the normal
specific heat may be traced to a small change in
bulk density of states which is very temperature
dependent.[12] However, even in the original AG
theory[f], the density of states in a superconductor
depends very much on whether self-energies are

computed self-consistently or not. In the Maki generalization[14] of Suhl's scattering equations for one impurity, true bound states[21] appear in the energy gap if the Kondo-Suhl temperature T_k is larger than T_{co} of the pure superconductor. Clearly these states will cease to exist in the gapless region. At the present time, we have no reliable estimates of how big the impurity concentration $n_i \equiv N_i/N$ may be before the above self-consistent effects become important, with the result that effect of the impurities on measurable quantities such as $\rho(\omega)$ is no longer linear in n_i.

In concluding these general remarks, I want to mention three other approaches to the Kondo problem which have the merit of a simple physical interpretation. One of these is to use a canonical transformation on the s - d interaction to get rid of it up to a certain order, replacing it by an effective interaction between the electrons and one between the impurity spins. To lowest order in J, this program has been carefully discussed in recent papers by Kim.[22] It would be interesting if one could extend this approach to get rid of $\hat{H}_{sd}$ to order J^2 - the effective interactions would then contain terms of order J^3 and hence the Kondo effect. We might note that Kim's effective exchange interaction between electrons (of order J^2) will tend to depress superconductivity by an amount

$$T_{co} - T_c \sim \frac{1}{\tau_s}[\ln(\frac{\omega_D}{T_{co}})]^2, \qquad (6)$$

to lowest order in n_i (ω_D is the mean phonon energy). This is quite different from the term picked up by the AG theory. It is a dynamical effect which arises

in the same way as the RKKY interaction between
impurities.

A second approach is to try and 'mutilate' the
commutation relations (4) sufficiently so as to able
to deal with (3) more simply. In a sense, Abrikosov[8]
did this with his pseudo-fermion representation. He
effectively reduced (3) to an interaction between two
kinds of fermions and thus could apply Feynmann
graphical techniques. Another well known case is
the bonon approximation to (4). This is clearly
discussed by Nakajima[23] for the case when every
atom in the crystal has a spin. Basically, $\hat{S}_z$ is
treated as a molecular field and $[\hat{S}_x, \hat{S}_y] \simeq iS$. The
interaction $\hat{H}_{sd}$ is eventually reduced to one coupling
conduction electrons and magnons. This leaves out
the Kondo effect (even if treated to all orders of
perturbation theory) since the latter depends cru-
cially on the fact that $[\hat{S}_x, \hat{S}_y]$ is an operator.
Nakajima's work can be generalized to superconductors, such as discussed by Dr. Bennemann in
this summer school.

Finally, there is the variational approach to
the Kondo effect. As an example, several authors[24]
choose a trial wave function corresponding to a
singlet,

$$|\psi> = \sum_k \{ \Gamma_{k\alpha}(a_{k\downarrow}{}^+\alpha) + \Gamma_{k\beta}(a_k{}_\uparrow{}^+\beta) \} \ |\psi>_o.$$

$$(7)$$

Here α and β represent spin up and spin down states
of the impurity ($S = \frac{1}{2}$), and $|\psi>_o$ is the filled Fermi
sea. One then determines $\Gamma_{k\alpha}$ and $\Gamma_{k\beta}$ so as to
minimize the total energy E. The decrease in energy
turns out to be of the order T_K. Up to about a year

ago, the Kondo-Suhl temperature was thought to be some sort of transition temperature (by anology to) T_c for a superconductor), rather than simply a temperature which sets the scale of energies in the Kondo effect. Thus it was natural to conclude that at $T \sim T_K$, a spin compensated (or quasi-bound) state appeared corresponding to a polarization cloud of electrons building up around the impurity with a range $\xi \simeq v_F/T_K$. For $T_K \simeq$ few ^{0}K, the "coherence" length ξ is of order 10^3Å. In my opinion, this popular picture of a spin compensated state[6] of very large range is not consistent with other calculations[25] (using the SAN theory) and can in no sense be considered as proven. Variational wave functions need not have any close contact with reality, even though they give good estimates of the energy. This variational approach has been generalized to include superconductors.[26] The decrease in the energy found in this case is presumably related to the true bound states found by Maki and Fowler.[14,21]

In Section II, we review some aspects of the Suhl-Abrikosov-Nagaoka theory for normal metals. As a concrete example, we discuss the first Kondo corrections to the electronic spin polarization around an impurity and the susceptibility.

In Section III, we discuss the generalization to superconductors. We shall mainly concentrate on the determination of T_c, which means we need only solve the scattering equations to first order in Δ (the Gor'kov order parameter). The equation for T_c depends only on the scattering amplitudes in the normal state. If we work to lowest order in impurity concentration, the previously mentioned "medium effect" may be neglected. The first Kondo corrections (of order J^3) to the properties of a superconductor are given explicitly. For the case of a single impurity spin, the novel aspects of the Kondo effect in superconductors are a straightforward consequence of a given energy gap ω_g in the unperturbed quasi-particle spectrum. One expects $\ln(D/\omega_g)$ to be involved in Kondo-type perturbation corrections. Much work, however, remains to be done in the case where we must self-consistently compute the renormalized excitation spectrum of the superconducting electrons.

We emphasize that our choice of references is only representative. Moreover, we think that in such a rapidly changing subject, the more recent literature is often the most useful.

II. SAN THEORY OF KONDO EFFECT IN NORMAL METALS

For simplicity, we shall discuss the SAN theory in terms of Suhl's scattering equations.[7] Suhl originally obtained these using dispersion theory, but it was later shown that Abrikosov's graphical technique led to the same equations.[11] In addition, Nagaoka's truncated equations of motion[9] can be shown to be completely equivalent, although somewhat less transparent, to Suhl's equations.[10] For a single magnetic impurity, the spin-flip $\tau(\omega)$ and non-spin flip $t(\omega)$ scattering applitudes are given by the following coupled, non-linear integral equations:

$$t(z + i0^+) = \frac{V}{N} + \int_{-\infty}^{\infty} \frac{dx}{z - x} \rho_0(x) \{ |t(x)|^2$$

$$+ \frac{S(S + 1)}{4} |\tau(x)|^2 \} \tag{8.1}$$

$$\tau(z + i0^+) = \frac{-J}{N} + \int_{-\infty}^{\infty} \frac{dx}{z - x} \, \rho_0(x) \, \{t(x)\, \tau^*(x)$$

$$+ t^*(x)\, \tau(x) - \frac{1}{2}\, |\tau(x)|^2 \tanh(\frac{\beta x}{2})\} . \tag{8.2}$$

We refer to Suhl's Varenna lectures[7] (see p. 170 ff.)
for a slightly more accurate version. We have assumed
that in addition to exchange scattering given by (3),
the impurity may give rise to potential scattering which
is well localized at the site. The total scattering matrix
is decomposed as follows:

$$T(z) = [t(z) + \frac{1}{2}\, S.\sigma\, \tau(z)]. \tag{9}$$

With the definitions Suhl used, $\tau(z) = 4\tau_{suhl}(z)$. That
the scattering amplitudes only depend on the energy
variable, without any dependence on the incoming and
outgoing momentum of the electrons, is ultimately due
to our working with delta-function interactions. This
produces a tremendous simplification into the theory.
As is well know, calculation of observable quantities
is much easier if the self-energies depend on ω but not
on k.

In Eqs. (8), $\rho_0(\omega)$ represents the free-particle
density of states (for one electron of energy ω)

$$\rho_0(\omega) = \frac{-1}{\pi} \int \frac{dk}{(2\pi)^3} \, \text{Im} \, G_0(k, \omega + i0^+) = \int \frac{dk}{(2\pi)^3} \, \delta(\epsilon_k - \omega). \tag{10}$$

Here $G_0(k, \omega)$ is the unperturbed Green's function,
and the kinetic energy ϵ_k, as usual, is measured with
respect to the Fermi energy $\epsilon_F = k_F^2/2m$. The integration in (10) can be rewritten as

$$\rho_0(\omega) = \int d\epsilon_k N_0(\epsilon_k) \delta(\epsilon_k - \omega), \qquad (11)$$

where $N_0(\epsilon_k)$ gives us the density of momentum states per unit energy interval. A simple approximation which is often used for $N_0(\epsilon)$ is the square free-particle state density

$$N_0 (\epsilon) = \frac{N}{4D}, \quad |\epsilon| < D$$

$$= 0, \quad |\epsilon| > D. \qquad (12)$$

Here N is the total number of electrons per unit volume and D is some band cutoff of the order of the Fermi energy. In his papers, Suhl[7] always used the parabolic density of states, $N_0(\epsilon) = m \sqrt{2m(\epsilon_F + \epsilon)}/2\pi^2$. Roughly speaking, this is equivalent to setting $D = \epsilon_F/3$ in Eq. (12). Probably the Lorentzian approximation[10-13] is the best in that it does not have any discontinuities. Since the Kondo divergences are related to a scattering resonance which occurs at energies very close to the Fermi energy (for $J < 0$), the actual form of $N_0(\epsilon)$ far away from the Fermi surface might not seem too critical. However this region does effect the exact solutions of (8) and some care must be exercised.

If one simply iterates Eqs. (8), one can generate a perturbation series for $t(\omega)$ and $\tau(\omega)$ in powers of J and V. For example, one finds [11,27,28] for the case $V = 0$,

$$t(\omega + i0^+) = -i\pi \frac{S(S + 1)}{4} \rho_0 \left(\frac{-J}{N}\right)^2 \{1 + 2\rho_0 \left(\frac{-J}{N}\right)g(\omega)$$

$$+ 3\left[\rho_0\left(\frac{-J}{N}\right)g(\omega)\right]^2 + \dots \} \qquad (13)$$

$$\tau(\omega) = \frac{-J}{N} \{ 1 + \rho_0 (\frac{-J}{N}) g(\omega) + \ldots \} \qquad (14)$$

where

$$g(\omega) \equiv \frac{-1}{2} \int_{-D}^{D} d\omega' \frac{\tanh(\beta \omega' 1/2)}{\omega - \omega' + i0^+} . \qquad (15)$$

We note that these results are consistent with the optical theorem

$$\mathrm{Im}\, t(\omega + i0^+) = -\pi \rho_0 [|t(\omega)|^2 + \frac{S(S + 1)}{4} |\tau(\omega)|^2], \qquad (16)$$

which is easily derived from (8.1). A direct perturbation calculation of the electronic transition probabil-
ity [proportional to $\mathrm{Im}\, t(\omega + i0^+)$] to third order in J
is given in §2 of Suhl's Varenna lectures[7], as well as in
Kondo's original paper. We strongly recommend
these elementary calculations to the reader for the
insight that they give into how the Kondo divergences
are related to (4) and why such divergences don't
arise for pure potential scattering.

The function $g(\omega)$ enters into higher order perturbation terms as well as the exact solution of Eqs. (8).
Falk and Fowler[29] first noted that it can be expressed
in terms of the digamma function $\Psi(x)$,

$$g(\omega) = \ln(\frac{D}{2\pi T}) - \Psi(\frac{1}{2} - \frac{i\omega}{2\pi T}) . \qquad (17)$$

In turn, a useful approximation is

$$-g(\omega) \cong \ln(\frac{\omega + iT}{iD}) = \ln(\frac{\sqrt{\omega^2 + T^2}}{D}) + \ln\left(\frac{1 - \dfrac{i\omega}{T}}{1 - \dfrac{i\omega}{T}}\right), \qquad (18)$$

as pointed out by Hamann.[27] Equation (18) correctly reproduces two important limits (to logarithmic accuracy)

$$g(\omega \ll T) \simeq -\ln\left(\frac{T}{D}\right) \qquad (19.1)$$

$$g(\omega \gg T) \simeq -\ln\left(\frac{\omega}{D}\right). \qquad (19.2)$$

Inserting (19) into (13), we see that the third order term in J in the forward-scattering amplitude diverges logarithmically as the electronic energy (relative to ϵ_F) or the temperature goes to zero. This essentially reproduces Kondo's original result. This divergence is removed by adding up the most divergent terms in each order of perturbation theory—this gives the Suhl-Abrikosov scattering equations (8). Clearly one must go to infinite order in J if the terms involving $g(\omega)$ in (13) and (14) are comparable to the Born terms. Thus the characteristic Kondo energy below which the first few perturbation terms are not sufficient is roughly given by

$$T_K \sim \omega_K \sim D \exp \frac{1}{(J\rho_1)}; \quad \rho_1 \equiv \frac{\rho_0}{N}. \qquad (20)$$

Note that our use of the rough approximation for the free density of states $\rho_0(\omega)$ is consistent with the band width 2D entering only logarithmically in $g(\omega)$. By the same token, the Kondo energy scale parameter given by (20) is a quantity which is defined by convention. This basic arbitrariness[6] of what we mean by the Kondo temperature should be remembered when one sees numerical estimates of T_K given in the experimental literature.

Equation (20) is the natural definition when one examines many crude solutions to the SAN theory, such as Hamann's expression[27] for the t-matrix

$$t(\omega) = + \frac{1}{2\pi i \rho_1 N} \left[1 - \frac{\left(1 + J\rho_1 \, g(\omega)\right)}{\left[|1 + J\rho_1 g(\omega)|^2 + \pi^2 S(S + 1)(J\rho_1)^2 \right]^{1/2}} \right] \quad (21)$$

In all derivations,[11] the SAN integral equations are obtained working to leading logarithmic order. More precisely, if the contributions to the scattering amplitudes are written in the form $(J\rho_1)^{n+m} |g(\omega)|^n$ ($n = 0, 1, 2, \ldots$, $m = 2, 3, \ldots$), then only the $m = 2$ terms are supposed to be relevant. This is reasonable since the exchange interaction is assumed to be weak ($J/D \ll 1$), but certainly not obviously correct. This brings up a very unsettling feature of the SAN theory—for it is clear that a straightforward iteration of the scattering equations (8) produces terms with $m = 3, 4, \ldots$. However, as Duke and Silverstein[28] first pointed out, the higher order logarithmic terms so generated do not agree with the results found by a direct graphical calculation. We refer to Keiter[11] for a detailed derivation of the $n = 1$, $m = 3$ term. As far as the leading ($m = 2$) logarithmic terms go, the linearized version of Suhl's equations[28] already give the correct results. Notwithstanding these facts, the exact solution[7,12,13] of the SAN theory depends very critically on the particular set of higher order logarithmic terms that are implicit in the non-linear scattering equations such as (8). Moreover, these higher order terms seem fairly sensitive to behavior far

away from the Fermi surface and hence to the free
electron band structure. At the present time, we can
only provisionally conclude that the SAN theory is
more accurate than its derivation implies. It is
amusing that such a basic quantity as the change in
the total energy due to the exchange interaction seems
to be related,[12] crudely speaking, to a small correction to the second term in the denominator of the expression in (21).

One of the interesting aspects of the SAN theory
is the way ordinary potential scattering enters. This
feature gives a natural explanation of the anomalous
thermoelectric power of dilute alloys. It should turn
out to be important in the case of superconductors
which, in the absence of exchange scattering, are not
effected by potential scattering from random impurities (Anderson's theorem[2]). Several authors have recently noted[10,30] that one can elegantly include the effect of V once we have solutions of (8) for $V = 0$. As
is well known, the t-matrix for potential scattering is
given by

$$t_V(\omega) = \frac{\dfrac{V}{N}}{1 - \dfrac{V}{N} \displaystyle\int_{-\infty}^{\infty} \frac{d\omega' N_0(\omega')}{\omega + io^+ - \omega'}} \simeq \frac{\dfrac{V}{N}}{1 + i\pi V \rho_1}$$

$$\equiv \frac{V}{N} \cos \eta e^{i\eta}. \tag{22}$$

Let us denote the solutions of (8) for $V = 0$ [but with
altered density of states $\tilde{\rho}_0(\omega) \equiv \rho_0(\omega) \cos^2 \eta$ in the
integrands] by $\tilde{t}(\omega)$ and $\tilde{T}(\omega)$. It then can be shown[10]
that the scattering amplitudes for finite V are given by

$$t(\omega) = \tilde{t}(\omega) \cos^2 \eta e^{2i\eta} - t_V(\omega)$$

$$\tau(\omega) = \tilde{\tau}(\omega) \cos^2 \eta e^{2i\eta}.$$

(23)

As an example, we need only replace ρ_1 by $\rho_1 \cos^2 \eta$ in Hamann's approximation to give the appropriate $\tilde{t}(\omega)$. For weak potentials, we have

$$\eta \equiv \tan^{-1} \pi V \rho_1 \cong \pi V \rho_1.$$

It is clear that $\text{Im}[t(\omega) + t_V(\omega)] \propto \cos 2\eta$ and hence it changes sign as η goes through $\pi/4$. For $J = 0$, Eq. (8.1) reduces to the usual result for potential scattering without any restriction to small $\rho_1 V$. It is likely that for $J \neq 0$, Eqs. (8) are correct for arbitrary $\rho_1 V$ but are restricted to $\rho_1 J \ll 1$.

In terms of the non-spin flip scattering amplitude, the single particle Green's function is given by

$$G_{\alpha\alpha'}(\mathbf{k}, \mathbf{k}'; \omega) = [G_0(k, \omega) \delta(\mathbf{k} - \mathbf{k}')$$

$$+ G_0(\mathbf{k}, \omega) t(\omega) G_0(\mathbf{k}', \omega)] \delta_{\alpha\alpha'},$$

(24)

for a single impurity spin at the origin. Here α represents the electronic spin degree of freedom. If we are dealing with N_i randomly positioned impurities, the total scattering amplitude is

$$T_{\mathbf{k}\mathbf{k}}(\omega) \simeq \frac{N_i t(\omega)}{1 - N_i G_0(\mathbf{k}, \omega) t(\omega)}$$

(25)

After averaging over the impurity positions, the Green's function is found to be

$$G(k, \omega) = [G^{-1}(k, \omega) - N_i t(\omega)]^{-1}.$$

(26)

Expanding the r.h.s of (26) in the number of impurities, to lowest order we obtain

$$G(k, \omega) = G_0(k, \omega) + N_i G_0(k, \omega) t(\omega) G_0(k, \omega), \quad (27)$$

a result which is often used in calculations of thermodynamic properties of dilute alloys. In the derivation of (25), the contributions of the so-called crossing graphs have been neglected. These arise from scatterings which involve two or more different impurities. Hence in the expansion of $t(\omega)$ in powers of the potential, they give a contribution which involves at least one more power of the impurity concentration, relative to the terms summed up to give (25). More precisely, to lowest order in the impurity concentration, the electronic self-energy is given correctly by (26),

$$\Sigma(k, \omega) = N_i t(\omega). \quad (28)$$

This is a stronger statement than (27).

The bulk electronic density-of-states is defined by (10) but with the true spectral density. Using (27) and the square density-of-states given in (12), one may easily verify that for $\omega \ll D$,

$$\rho(\omega) = \rho_0 \left[1 - N_i \left(\frac{2}{\pi} \right) \frac{\text{Im } t(\omega)}{D} \right] \equiv \rho_0 + \delta\rho(\omega). \quad (29)$$

The correction is of order $\Sigma(\omega)/D$, which is generally very small. As one might expect, the actual form of $\delta\rho(\omega)$ is farily sensitive to what sort of state-density $N_0(\epsilon)$ we use for the free electron gas. In addition, different results may arise if we use (26) and then expand the result to lowest order in N_i. However, the

Lorentzian state-density gives the same expression
for $\delta\rho(\omega)$ via either (26) or (27), and it is proportional to Im $t(\omega)$, just as in (29). We conclude that electron tunneling measures the same quantity that most
transport properties probe. We recall that from
numerical calculations of Suhl and Wong,[7] Im $t(\omega)$
has a strong resonance at low energies. However,
it seems that the predicted specific heat anomaly[12,13]
in the Kondo problem comes about because Im $t(\omega)$
is very temperature dependent, rather than because
Im $t(\omega)$ becomes large. The maximum value of $t(\omega)$
is given by the unitarity limit, i.e., $t(\omega) = (\pi i \rho_0)^{-1}$.
Substituting this into (29), we see that the maximum
value of $\delta\rho/\rho_0$ is $\simeq n_i$.

Due to the relatively small change in $\rho(\omega)$, we
need not worry about trying to solve a self-consistent version of Suhl's equations using $\rho(\omega)$ given by
(29) in place of the unperturbed value $\rho_0(\omega)$. To first
order in n_i, it is sufficient to use the zero order expression for $t(\omega)$ [The case of superconductors is quite
different due to the strong effect of the magnetic impurities on the density of states—for example, the
energy gap is completely removed]. As we have mentioned in the introduction, Nagaoka[20] has tried to generalize his equations of motion approach to the case
of many independent impurities. The functions which
appear in Nagaoka's equations, as well as the form of
the latter, do not suggest a very natural or obvious
way in which to effect the inclusion of self-consistent
impurity effects. In this regard, the Suhl-Abrikosov
formulation of the scattering equations is much better.
In any event, Nagaoka was led to

$$\omega - N_i \, \tilde{t}(\omega) \equiv \tilde{\omega}(\omega) = \omega - N_i \, t(\tilde{\omega}), \tag{30}$$

where $t(\omega)$ is the t-matrix for a single impurity. On examining Eqs. (8), it is clear that this corresponds to replacing t by $\tilde{t}$, and z in the integrand denominators by $\tilde{z}(z)$ defined self-consistently as in (30). However, Keiter's derivation[11] of Suhl's equations indicates that the correct renormalization procedure is rather to replace $\rho_0(x)$ by $\rho_0(\tilde{x})$ in the integrand numerators (and of course, interpret t and $\tilde{t}$ wherever it appears). As we discussed in the preceding paragraph, we expect $\rho_0(\tilde{x}) \simeq \rho_0$ and hence $\tilde{t}(\omega) \simeq t(\omega)$. This is in great contrast to Nagaoka's result (30).

For a greater understanding of the Kondo anomalous scattering, it is clearly desirable to study the local electronic charge and spin density induced around on impurity spin. Everts and Ganguly[25] have recently given a careful treatment of these questions. The spin polarization $P(r)$ at a distance $\mathbf{r}$ from an impurity spin in a weak magnetic field H is given by

$$\langle s_z^{el}(\mathbf{r}) \rangle_H \equiv P(r) = \frac{g\mu_B H}{3T} \{ \langle s^{el}(\mathbf{r}) \cdot s^{el} \rangle_0$$

$$+ \langle s^{el}(\mathbf{r}) \cdot S \rangle_0 \}. \tag{30}$$

where

$$s^{el} = \int d\mathbf{r} s^{el}(\mathbf{r}).$$

In contrast, the static susceptibility χ is the linear response of the total spin,

$$\chi = \frac{(\mu_B g)^2}{3T} \left\{ \langle s^{el} \cdot s^{el} \rangle_0 + 2 \langle s^{el} \cdot S \rangle_0 \right.$$

$$\left. + S(S+1) \right\}. \tag{32}$$

In some sense, the key quantity in both (31) and (32) is the electronic spin-spin correlation function

$$\langle \mathbf{s}^{el}(r) \cdot \mathbf{s}^{el} \rangle_0.$$

One can reduce (32) to

$$\chi = \chi_{pauli} + \frac{(\mu_B g)^2}{3T}(1 + J\rho_1)[S(S + 1) + \langle \mathbf{s}^{el} \cdot \mathbf{S} \rangle_0]$$

$$\equiv \chi_{pauli} + \mu_B g\left(\frac{\langle S_z \rangle_H}{H}\right)(1 + J\rho_1). \tag{33}$$

Now by explicit calculation, $\langle \mathbf{s}^{el}(r) \cdot \mathbf{S} \rangle_0$ gives rise to the well known Rudermann-Kittel-Yosida oscillatory polarization to first order in $J\rho_1$. However, in the terms proportional to $(J\rho_1)^2$, in addition to a RKY-type oscillatory contribution, there is a term which goes as $(k_F r)^{-3}$. It is the latter non-oscillatory part which produces a logarithmically divergent contribution to

$$\int d\mathbf{r} \, \langle \mathbf{s}^{el}(\mathbf{r}) \cdot \mathbf{S} \rangle_0$$

and hence the susceptibility in (33).

Oddly enough, it turns out that $\langle \mathbf{s}^{el}(\mathbf{r}) \cdot \mathbf{s}^{el} \rangle_0 = -\langle \mathbf{s}^{el}(\mathbf{r}) \cdot \mathbf{S} \rangle_0 +$ (fairly well behaved oscillatory terms). Thus the non-oscillatory terms which already appear in $\langle \mathbf{s}^{el}(r) \cdot \mathbf{S} \rangle_0$ in second order do not contribute directly to the polarization cloud. The work of Everts and Ganguly suggests that, basically, the polarization around an impurity has the RKY form but with an amplitude proportional to $\langle S_z \rangle_H (3T/H)$ rather than $S(S + 1)$. The effective value of the impurity spin $\langle S_z \rangle_H$

is defined by (33) and is directly related to the static susceptibility. This picture does not agree with the very popular picture óf a long range polarization which is always negative, or antiparallel to the impurity spin.

In concluding this section, we recall that throughout we have neglected the internal magnetic fields $\overline{H}$ arising from the RKKY impurity coupling. These would give rise to Zeeman splittings of the impurity spin levels. Roughly speaking, these would have the effect of making the logarithmic terms such as (19.2) involve $\omega + g\mu_B\overline{H}$ in place of ω.

III. MAKI-SUHL THEORY OF KONDO EFFECT IN SUPERCONDUCTORS

Maki[14] has formulated the problem of a magnetic impurity in a superconductor using the dispersion theoretic approach of Suhl. For the special case of $V = 0$, his scattering equations are very similar to those for a normal metal.

We first recall that in the Gor'kov approximation, a superconductor with translational symmetry is described by the ordinary Green's function

$$G_{\uparrow\uparrow}(\mathbf{k}, i\omega_n) = -\frac{i\widetilde{\omega}_n + \epsilon_k}{\widetilde{\omega}_n^2 + \epsilon_k^2 + \widetilde{\Delta}_n^2} \qquad (33)$$

and the anomalous Green's function

$$F_{\uparrow\downarrow}(\mathbf{k}, i\omega_n) = \frac{\widetilde{\Delta}_n}{\widetilde{\omega}_n^2 + \epsilon_k^2 + \widetilde{\Delta}_n^2}. \qquad (34)$$

In terms of the 2 x 2 Nambu space, G and F are the diagonal and off-diagonal elements. The corresponding renormalized energies are given by

$$\tilde{\omega}_n(\omega_n) = \omega_n + \Sigma_d(\omega_n) \tag{35}$$

$$\tilde{\Delta}_n(\omega_n) = \Delta + \Sigma_{od}(\omega_n), \tag{36}$$

where $\Sigma(\omega_n)$ represents the change due to the inter-action (in addition to the attractive pairing force, whose contribution is Δ). The Gor'kov order parameter Δ is self-consistently determined by the so-called gap equation

$$\Delta = |g| T \sum_{n=-\infty}^{\infty} \int \frac{dk}{(2\pi)^3} F_{\uparrow\downarrow}(k, \omega_n). \tag{37}$$

We have of course assumed that all the interactions give rise to self-energies which are only weakly dependent on the momentum of the electrons, although they may depend on the energy variable $\omega_n = (2n + 1)\pi T$. The normal density of states for energy ω is

$$\rho(\omega) \equiv -\frac{1}{\pi} \int \frac{dk}{(2\pi)^3} \, \text{Im} \, G_{\uparrow\uparrow}(k, i\omega_n \to \omega + io^+)$$

$$= -\text{Im}\left(\frac{u}{\sqrt{1-u^2}}\right) N_0 \tag{38}$$

where $u(\omega) \equiv i\tilde{\omega}_n(\omega)/\tilde{\Delta}_n(\omega)$ and we made an analytic continuation from the discrete imaginary energies to the real axis from above. Similarly, the anomalous density of states is given by

$$f(\omega) \equiv -\frac{1}{\pi} \int \frac{dk}{(2\pi)^3} \, \text{Im} \, F_{\uparrow\downarrow}(k, i\omega_n \to \omega + io^+)$$

$$= -\text{Im}\left(\frac{1}{\sqrt{1-u^2}}\right) N_0. \tag{39}$$

Performing the momentum integration in (37), we may reduce the gap equation to[2]

$$\Delta = 2\pi |g| N_0 T \sum_{n=0}^{\infty} \frac{\tilde{\omega}_n}{\sqrt{\tilde{\omega}_n^2 + \tilde{\Delta}_n^2}}. \tag{40}$$

We note that Δ only depends on the ratio $u_n \equiv \tilde{\omega}_n/\tilde{\Delta}_n$, as do all equilibrium properties of a superconductor with self-energies which are momentum-independent. In the limit $\Delta \to 0$ (i.e., $T \to T_c$), one sees that u_n (and its analytic continuation u) becomes very large. The equation for the transition temperature found from (40) may be conveniently written as

$$\ln\left(\frac{T_c}{T_{c0}}\right) = 2\pi T_c \sum_{n=0}^{\infty} \left(\frac{1}{\Delta u_n^0} - \frac{1}{\omega_n}\right)\Bigg|_{T=T_c}. \tag{41}$$

Here $u_n^0 = \tilde{\omega}_n^0/\tilde{\Delta}_n^0$, where $\tilde{\omega}_n^0$ is computed in the limit $\Delta \to 0$ (normal state) while $\tilde{\Delta}_n^0$ is the leading term proportional to Δ.

We now specialize our discussion to the self-energies due to exchange scattering from impurities. The original Abrikosov-Gor'kov theory was a theory for many randomly positioned impurities. The averaging over positions restored translational symmetry, with the result that the Green's functions were of the kind given in (33) and (34). The order parameter entering into the theory involved an impurity average, and thus is independent of position. The self-consistent Born approximation to the self-energies for real frequencies ($i\omega_n \to \omega + io^+$) is

$$i \sum_d (\omega) = \left(\frac{1}{2\tau_v} + \frac{1}{2\tau_s}\right) \frac{1}{\sqrt{\tilde{\Delta}^2 - \tilde{\omega}^2}} \tag{42}$$

$$\Sigma_{od}(\omega) = (\frac{1}{2\tau_v} - \frac{1}{2\tau_s}) \frac{\tilde{\Delta}}{\sqrt{\tilde{\Delta}^2 - \tilde{\omega}^2}} \, , \quad (43)$$

where the relaxation times for both potential and spin scattering are included. We recall that in this case, the function u is the solution of the famous equation

$$\frac{\omega}{\Delta} = u(1 - \xi \frac{1}{\sqrt{1 - u^2}}), \quad (44)$$

where the so-called depairing parameter is defined by $\xi \equiv (\tau_s \Delta)^{-1}$. By considering ω/Δ as a function of real u, it is clear that the energy gap ω_g corresponds to the maximum in this curve for $0 < u < 1$, since the density of states is proportional to the imaginary part of u. This gives

$$\omega_g = \Delta (1 - \xi^{2/3})^{3/2} \qquad \xi < 1$$
$$= 0 \qquad\qquad\qquad \xi < 1. \qquad (45)$$

For further details, we refer to Maki's review.[2]

There are several aspects of the AG theory which are very relevant to our later generalization of it to include the Kondo effect. First of all, even though the self-energies are lowest order in impurity concentration n_i, the measurable properties of the superconducting alloy (such as $\omega_g, \rho(\omega)$, etc.) are highly non-linear in n_i. This is most clearly seen in the dependence of these quantities on the depairing parameter ξ. No matter how small n_i is, ξ is greater than unity for temperatures sufficiently close to T_c and the excitation spectrum is then gapless. The second point is that in the limit $\Delta \rightarrow 0$,

$$u_n = u_n^0 \simeq \frac{\omega_n + \frac{1}{\tau_s}}{\Delta} - \frac{1}{2\tau_s} \frac{\Delta}{(\omega_n + 1/\tau_s)^2} + \cdots \tag{46}$$

and hence the implicit equation

$$\ln\left(\frac{T_c}{T_{co}}\right) = 2 \sum_{n=0}^{\infty} \left(\frac{1}{2n+1} - \frac{1}{2n+1+\frac{1}{\pi T_c \tau_s}} \right) \tag{47}$$

determines T_c. If we expand the r.h.s to lowest order in n_i, we obtain the result given in (1). If we had not computed the self-energies self-consistently with the true 2 x 2 Nambu propagator, we would find

$$\tilde{\omega} = \omega + \left(\frac{1}{2\tau_v} + \frac{1}{2\tau_s}\right) \frac{\omega}{\sqrt{\Delta^2 - \omega^2}} \tag{48}$$

$$\tilde{\Delta} = \Delta + \left(\frac{1}{2\tau_v} - \frac{1}{2\tau_s}\right) \frac{\Delta}{\sqrt{\Delta^2 - \omega^2}}$$

in place of (42) and (43). Instead of (44), the ratio of these renormalized energies is

$$u \equiv \frac{\tilde{\omega}}{\tilde{\Delta}} = \frac{\omega}{\Delta} \left\{ \frac{1 + \frac{1}{2}\left(\frac{1}{\tau_v} + \frac{1}{\tau_s}\right) \frac{1}{\sqrt{\Delta^2 - \omega^2}}}{1 + \frac{1}{2}\left(\frac{1}{\tau_v} - \frac{1}{\tau_s}\right) \frac{1}{\sqrt{\Delta^2 - \omega^2}}} \right\} \tag{49}$$

The dependence of u on τ_v clearly indicates that this result is only valid to lowest order in n_i. In this limit, both (44) and (49) give the same expression

$$u = \frac{\tilde{\omega}}{\tilde{\Delta}} (1 + \frac{1}{\tau_s} \frac{1}{\sqrt{\Delta^2 - \omega^2}}),$$ (50)

as we would expect. However, it is easy to verify that if we use (50), the energy gap ω_g is always equal to Δ and thus if we work to lowest order in n_i, we never get gapless superconductivity. This problem arises because the expansion parameter is $(\tau_s\Delta)^{-1}$ rather than τ_s^{-1}. Eq. (50) gives the correct depression in T_c because the transition temperature does not depend on the excitation spectrum of the superconducting state. The great accuracy of the AG theory gives strong support to the validity of the procedure of computing electronic self-energies to lowest order in the impurity concentration but with self-consistent propagators. The formal justification of this procedure is, of course, non-trivial.

The problem of a <u>single</u> impurity spin in an superconductor has been discussed by several authors treating the exchange interaction to lowest order. We refer to Heinrichs[31] for a careful discussion near T_c, and for earlier references. For $T \sim T_c$, he finds that the order parameter $\Delta(r)$ at a distance $r(\gg \xi_0)$ from the impurity is given by

$$[\Delta(r) - \Delta(\infty)] \sim (\frac{l_s}{\xi_0})^2 (\frac{\xi_0}{r}) e^{-2(r/\xi_0)}.$$ (51)

Here l_s is the exchange scattering mean free path and ξ_0 is the B.C.S. coherence length. At smaller distances, RKY-type oscillations develop. This local depression in the Cooper pair density near the impurity spin site has been left out of the AG theory (the latter only includes the decrease in the uniform order parameter due to the renormalization effects of the impurities on the electrons). However, the local depression in $\Delta(r)$ has a very small effect on T_c.[31]

We are now ready to write down the Maki-Suhl scattering equations for a superconductor, which generalize the AG theory to the extent that the exchange interaction with a single impurity is treated to all orders. It is convenient to define some auxiliary functions as follows:

$$\tilde{\Delta}(\omega) - \Delta = -\frac{1}{2} \left[t_+(\omega) - t_-(\omega) \right] \tag{52}$$

$$\tilde{\omega}(\omega) - \omega = -\frac{1}{2} \left[t_+(\omega) + t_-(\omega) \right].$$

For $V = 0$, Maki finds

$$t_\pm(z + i0^+) = \int_{-\infty}^{\infty} \frac{dx}{z - x} \rho_\pm(x) \left\{ |t_\pm(x)|^2 + \frac{S(S+1)}{4} | \tau_\pm(x)|^2 \right\}, \tag{53}$$

where the two new functions $\tau_\pm(x)$ are given by the dispersion relations

$$\tau_\pm(z + i0^+) = \frac{-J}{N} + \int_{-\infty}^{\infty} \frac{dx}{z - x} \rho_\pm(x) \left\{ t_\pm(x) \tau_\pm{}^*(x) \right.$$

$$\left. + t_\pm{}^*(x) \tau_\pm(x) - \frac{1}{2} \tanh \frac{\beta x}{2} | \tau_\pm(x)|^2 \right\}. \tag{54}$$

The new density of states $\rho_\pm(x)$ in these equations is

$$\rho_\pm(x) \equiv [\rho(x) \pm f(x)],   \tag{55}$$

where for one impurity, $\rho(\omega)$ and $f(\omega)$ are given by the usual B.C.S. expressions [see Eqs. (38) and (39) for the general definition of the densities]. We note that $\rho_\pm(x) = 0$ for $|x| > \omega_g$.

In order to make contact with direct perturbation calculations[26], we simply iterate (53) and (54). Using a square free particle state-density, we have to second order in J

$$t_\pm(z) = N_0 \frac{S(S+1)}{4} \int_R \frac{dx}{z-x} \left(\frac{x \pm \Delta}{\sqrt{x^2 - \Delta^2}}\right) |\tau_\pm(x)|^2,   \tag{56}$$

where

$$\tau_\pm(z) = \frac{-J}{N} + N_0\left(\frac{J}{N}\right)^2 \int_R \frac{dx}{z-x} \left(\frac{x \pm \Delta}{\sqrt{x^2 - \Delta^2}}\right)\left(-\frac{1}{2}\tanh\frac{\beta x}{2}\right).   \tag{57}$$

The subscript R on the integrals means that they are restricted to $|x| >$ energy gap, which is simply Δ since we have omitted all renormalization corrections to $\rho_\pm(x)$. The integrals involved in (56) and (57) have been discussed in detail by Maki and Fowler[21] since they appear in the exact solutions of (53) and (54) as well. The function analogous to $g(\omega)$ [see (15)] in the normal state is

$$A_\pm (z, T) \equiv -\frac{1}{2} \int_R \frac{dx}{z - x} \, \text{Re} \left(\frac{x \pm \Delta}{\sqrt{x^2 - \Delta^2}} \right) \tanh \frac{1}{2} \beta x$$

$$= \int_\Delta^D \frac{dx}{\sqrt{x^2 - \Delta^2}} \, \tanh \frac{1}{2} \beta x \qquad (58)$$

$$+ z(z \pm \Delta) \int_\Delta^D \frac{dx}{\sqrt{x^2 - \Delta^2}} \, \frac{1}{x^2 - z^2} \tanh \frac{1}{2} \beta x.$$

We recall that in the B.C.S. theory, the temperature dependent gap parameter Δ is determined by the implicit equation

$$\int_\Delta^{\omega_D} \frac{dx}{\sqrt{x^2 - \Delta^2}} \, \tanh \frac{1}{2} \beta x = \ln \left(\frac{2\omega_D}{\Delta_0} \right), \qquad (59)$$

where $\Delta_0 = (\pi/\gamma) T_{co}$ is the energy gap at $0°K$. Thus the first integral on the r.h.s. of (58) is simply equal to $\ln (2D/\Delta_0)$ at all temperatures. The second integral is worked out for various temperatures in the appendix of ref. 21 for $|z| < \Delta$. Restricting ourselves to $0°K$ and assuming that $D \gg \Delta, |z|$, we find for $|z| > \Delta$

$$\text{Re } A_\pm(z, 0) = \ln \left(\frac{2D}{\Delta_0} \right) - \frac{(z \pm \Delta)}{\sqrt{z^2 - \Delta^2}} \, \text{arccosh} \left| \frac{z}{\Delta} \right|. (60)$$

Taking the imaginary part of Eq. (56) gives

$$\text{Im } t_\pm(z) = -\pi \rho_0 \frac{S(S + 1)}{4} \left(\frac{J}{N} \right)^2 \frac{z \mp \Delta}{\sqrt{z^2 - \Delta^2}} \left| 1 \right.$$

$$+ \rho_0 \frac{-J}{N} A_\pm(z, T) \Big|^2. \qquad (61)$$

Making use of (60) and the relations in (52), we have

$$\widetilde{\omega} = \omega + \frac{i}{2\tau_s} \frac{\omega}{\sqrt{\omega^2 - \Delta_0^2}} \left\{ 1 + 2\rho_0 \left(\frac{-J}{N}\right) \left[\ln\left(\frac{2D}{\Delta_0}\right) \right. \right.$$

$$\left. \left. - \frac{1}{\omega}\sqrt{\omega^2 - \Delta_0^2} \; \text{arccosh} \left| \frac{\omega}{\Delta_0} \right| \right] \; \ldots \right\} \quad (62)$$

$$\widetilde{\Delta} = \Delta_0 - \frac{i}{2\tau_s} \frac{\Delta_0}{\sqrt{\omega^2 - \Delta_0^2}} \left\{ 1 + 2\rho_0 \left(\frac{-J}{N}\right) \ln\left(\frac{2D}{\Delta_0}\right) + \ldots \right\}, \quad (63)$$

where τ_s is the Born approximation to the exchange scattering time. We have simply multiplied the self-energies by the number of impurities. Clearly Eqs. (62) and (63) to lowest order in J reproduce the Abrikosov-Gor'kov results given in (48). Generally, the real parts of the self-energies are assumed to be of negligible importance—they may be easily found by working out the integral in (56) explicitly instead of using (61). For $|\omega| \gg \Delta_0$, Eq. (62) simplifies to

$$\widetilde{\omega} = \omega + \left(\frac{i}{2\tau_s}\right) \text{sgn} \, \omega \left\{ 1 + 2\rho_0 \left(\frac{-J}{N}\right) \ln\frac{D}{|\omega|} + \ldots \right\}. \quad (64)$$

The effective lifetime in (64) is seen to be the same expression as found in normal metals to order J^3 [see Eqs. (13) and (14)], as we would expect in the limit of high energies.

Near the transition temperature T_c, we can work to lowest order in Δ. In this case, $A_\pm(z, T) \approx g(z, T)$ and hence

$$\tilde{\omega}_n \simeq \omega_n + \frac{1}{2\tau_s} \left\{ 1 + 2\rho_1(-J)g(i\omega_n) \right\} + 0(\Delta) \tag{65}$$

$$\tilde{\Delta}_n \simeq \Delta - \frac{1}{2\tau_s} \left(\frac{\Delta}{\omega_n} \right) \left\{ 1 + 2\rho_1(-J)g(i\omega_n) \right\} + 0(\Delta^2),$$

and thus

$$\Delta u_n^0 \simeq \omega_n + \frac{1}{\tau_s} \left[1 + 2\rho_1(-J)g(i\omega_n) \right]. \tag{66}$$

We note that the first Kondo correction has the same effect on both self-energies. Here $g(i\omega_n)$ is the function defined in Eq. (15). For reasons discussed earlier, (66) is only correct to lowest order in the impurity concentration. Inserting (66) into Eq. (41) leads to the following initial depression in the transition temperature:

$$T_{co} - T_c \simeq \frac{2}{\pi\tau_s} \left\{ \frac{\pi^2}{8} + 2\rho_1 J \sum_{n=0}^{\infty} \frac{g(i\omega_n^c)}{(2n+1)^2} \right\}$$

$$\simeq \frac{\pi}{4\tau_s} \left\{ 1 + 2\rho_1(-J)\ln\left(\frac{D}{T_{co}} \right) \right. \tag{67}$$

$$\left. + \text{ terms of order } (\rho_1(-J)) \right\}.$$

Since $D \gg T_{cp}$, we are justified in neglecting the non-logarithmic terms in order J^3. The first Kondo correction to the initial decrease in T_c predicted by Eq. (1) is identical to the first correction to the normal state reciprocal relaxation time. Several expressions given in the literature[14,15,32] reduce to (67) in the appropriate limit.

We have discussed the first Kondo corrections (in order J^3) predicted by the Maki-Suhl scattering equations. More generally, one can write down exact solutions in analogy to the discussions of similar equations in the normal state.[10, 14] Since $\Delta \to 0$, the initial decrease in T_c can be reduced to expressions only involving the normal state scattering matrices. To vanishing order in Δ, we have

$$\widetilde{\omega} \simeq \omega - iN_i \, \mathrm{Im} \, t_N(\omega) + \dots \tag{68}$$

where the subscript N refers to the solutions of Suhl's equations for one impurity in the normal state. To first order in Δ, the off-diagonal self-energy is

$$\widetilde{\Delta}_n \simeq \Delta[1 - N_i \, \mathrm{Im} \, A(\omega)] + \dots \tag{69}$$

where the function $A(\omega)$ is the solution of the linear, singular integral equations

$$A(z) = \frac{t_N(z)}{z} + 2\rho_0 \int_{-D}^{D} \frac{dx}{z-x} \, [\mathrm{Re}\{t_N^*(x)A(x)\}$$

$$+ \frac{S(S+1)}{4} \, \mathrm{Re}\{\tau_N^*(x)B(x)\}] \tag{70}$$

$$B(z) = \frac{\left(\tau_N - \frac{-J}{N}\right)}{2} + 2\rho_0 \int_{-D}^{D} \frac{dx}{z-x} \, \Big[\mathrm{Re}\{\tau_N^*(x)A(x)\}$$

$$+ \mathrm{Re}\{t_N(x)B(x)\} \tag{71}$$

$$- \frac{1}{2} \tanh\left(\frac{\beta x}{2}\right)\{\mathrm{Re} \, \tau_N^*(x)B(x)\}\Big].$$

These are easily iterated to give $A(z)$ up to any order in J, once we know $\tau_N(\omega)$ and $t_N(\omega)$.

The solution of Eqs. (53) and (54) in a form equivalent to Hamann's approximate solution for the normal state [see Eq. (21)] is

$$t_\pm^S(\omega) = \frac{1}{2\pi i\rho_\pm}\left\{1 - \frac{[1 + \rho_0\left(\frac{J}{N}\right)A_\pm(\omega, T)]}{\{|1 + \rho_0\left(\frac{J}{N}\right)A_\pm(\omega, T)|^2}\right.$$

$$\left. + \pi^2 S(S + 1)\left(\rho_\pm\frac{J}{N}\right)^2\right\}^{1/2}\right\} \quad (72)$$

Several features of the exact solutions[12,13] are shared by this simple approximation. I feel that this simplicity is ample justification for using it in these lectures in order to find a non-perturbative expression for the depression in T_c. In order to find $(t_+^S - t_-^S)$ to first order in Δ, it is sufficient to use

$$A_\pm(\omega, T_c) \simeq \frac{1}{2}\int_{-D}^{D}\frac{dx}{x - z}\tanh(\frac{1}{2}\beta x)(1 \pm \frac{\Delta}{x})$$

$$= g(\omega) \pm \frac{\Delta}{\omega}[g(\omega) - g(0)]. \quad (73)$$

A straightforward expansion $t_\pm^S(\omega)$ in powers of Δ gives, after some algebra,

$$\tilde{\Delta}_n \simeq \Delta - \frac{\Delta}{\omega_n} \frac{N_i}{2\pi\rho_0}$$

$$\times \left[1 + \left\langle \{ |X(\omega_n^c)|^2 + \pi^2 S(S+1) \} \times \right. \right. \tag{74}$$

$$\{ (\text{sign } J) \text{Re } X(\omega_n^c) - X(0) \}$$

$$\left. \left. + [\text{Re } X(\omega_n^c)]^2 X(0) / \{ |X(\omega_n^c)|^2 + \pi^2 S(S+1) \}^{3/2} \right] \right.$$

where now $\omega_n^c = (2n+1)\pi T_c$ and we have introduced a new function which naturally arises in the theory,

$$X(\omega_n) \equiv - \frac{1}{J\rho_1} [1 + J\rho_1 \, g(i\omega_n)]$$

$$= \ln\left(\frac{T}{T_K}\right) + \Psi\left(\frac{1}{2} + \frac{\omega_n}{2\pi T}\right) - \Psi\left(\frac{1}{2}\right) \tag{75}$$

$$= \ln\left(\frac{T}{T_K}\right) + \Psi(1+n) - \Psi\left(\frac{1}{2}\right).$$

We also have

$$\tilde{\omega}_n \simeq \omega_n + \frac{N_i}{2\pi\rho_0} \left[1 + \frac{(\text{sign } J) \text{Re} X(\omega_n)}{[\, |X(\omega_n)|^2 + \pi^2 S(S+1)\,]^{1/2}} \right]. \tag{76}$$

Following usual practice, for mathematical convenience, we have defined the Kondo temperature appearing in (75) as

$$T_K = \frac{2\gamma}{\pi} D \exp\left(\frac{1}{J\rho_1}\right). \tag{77}$$

We recall that

$$\Psi\left(\frac{1}{2}\right) = -\ln 4\gamma, \text{ where } \gamma \simeq 1.78.$$

Taking the ratio of (74) to (76), we find the initial decrease in the superconducting transition temperature is simply

$$\Delta T_c \simeq \frac{N_i}{\pi^2 \rho_0} \sum_{n=0} \frac{1}{2n+1}$$

$$\times \frac{X(0)\pi^2 S(S+1)}{\left\{ |X(\omega_n^c)|^2 + \pi^2 S(S+1) \right\}^{3/2}} \tag{78}$$

We note that (78) is somewhat different from the expressions originally given by Griffin [32] and Maki. [14] Section V of ref. 14 contains an error which when corrected leads to results similar to (78). [33] The function $X(\omega_n^c)$ defined in Eq. (75) may be considered as a function of $\ln(T_c/T_K)$, which in turn is a measure of the relative strength of the pairing and exchange interactions. In the following discussion we shall assume $J < 0$, since $-\ln(T_c/T_K)$ is always very large for $J > 0$.

According to Eq. (76), the imaginary part of the normal state electronic self-energy increases in magnitude and then levels off to the value given by unitarity as $X(\omega_n^c)$ goes from ∞ to $-\infty$. We recall that the tunneling density of states is determined by $\text{Im} t(\omega)$ and the electrical conductivity by $\text{Im} t(\omega = 0)$. Recent numerical calculations of $\text{Im} t(\omega)$ using the exact solutions of the SAN equations have been

performed by Everts and Chow. They found that the
resonance is always at the Fermi energy ($\omega = 0$),
contrary to earlier work of Suhl and Wong (see
ref. 7), who found a resonance asymmetrically
positioned with respect to the Fermi Surface.

According to Eq. (78), the initial slope of the
transition temperature vs concentration curve is
directly proportional to $X(0) = \ln(T_{co}/T_K)$, which is
negative for $T_{co} < T_K$. This would imply that for a
given T_{co}, the transition temperature T_c would first
decrease then increase, eventually becoming larger
than T_{co}. According to Maki[33], this anomalous behaviour indicates that the expansion in powers of the
order parameter breaks down at $T_K = T_{co}$, and
hence (78) is only valid for T_{co} somewhat larger
than T_K. The terms in the series in Eq. (78) decrease rapidly as a result of the factor $(2n + 1)^{-2}$
and thus a good estimate might be made by considering only the $n = 0$ term. Since the important
energies are of order T_{co}, we are not obviously
justified in using either of the simple approximations given by (19.1) and (19.2). However, a good
estimate of the initial change in T_c predicted by
Eq. (78) may be found using $X(\omega_n c) \approx \ln(T_{co}/T_K)$,
omitting any consideration of the non-logarithmic
terms. Thus we obtain the simple analytic expression

$$\Delta T_c \equiv (T_{co} - T_c) \tag{79}$$

$$\simeq \frac{\ln(T_{co}/T_K)}{\{[\ln(T_{co}/T_K)]^2 + \pi^2 S(S+1)\}^{3/2}} \cdot \frac{N_i}{8N_o},$$

which may be experimentally tested.

In principle, the Zuckermann-Nagaoka theory[15] of the Kondo effect in superconductors should lead to the same results as obtained with the Maki-Suhl theory, since the equivalence of the two discussions in the normal state has been proven. However, Zuckermann includes the self-consistent medium effects in the same way as Nagaoka did.[20] We believe that for the reasons mentioned in Section II, the correct generalization is to use the renormalized density of states[14] in Eqs. (53) and (54). Zuckermann found that the initial depression in T_{co} reached a maximum for $T_{co} \sim T_K$, contrary to what we found above.

Maki has written down the scattering equations for a superconductor when there is both potential and exchange scattering. In the notation of Section II of ref. 14,

$$\tilde{\omega} = \omega - \frac{iN_i}{2} \text{Im}[t_+(\omega) + t_-(\omega) + L_+(\omega) + L_-(\omega)] \tag{81}$$

$$\tilde{\Delta} = \Delta + \frac{iN_i}{2} \text{Im}[t_+(\omega) - t_-(\omega) + L_+(\omega) - L_-(\omega)]. \tag{82}$$

It is a straightforward task to iterate the scattering equations given in Eq. (26) of ref. 14. One finds that the change in the transition temperature will be proportional to terms like J^2V^2 and J^3V^3 in lowest non-trivial order in V. The effect of these terms on the superconducting properties generally should be of some experimental interest and a more detailed analysis will be given elsewhere.

In conclusion, we would like to make a few remarks about the bound states which appear in the energy gap. The original discussion in Section III of ref. 14 has been corrected by Maki and Fowler.[21] The latter authors show by a very elegant technique that as we increase $\ln(T_k/T_{co})$, two poles appear at energies Δ and $-\Delta$ (relative to ϵ_F) when $T_k = T_{co}$. As the ratio T_k/T_{co} continues to increase, the bound state at Δ moves towards $-\Delta$ and the one at $-\Delta$ moves towards Δ. The strength of these bound states was not computed and, in any event, this would depend very much on using the renormalized density of states $\rho(\omega)$ and $f(\omega)$ in Eqs. (53) and (54). We might remark that these bound states at energies $|z| < \Delta$ must be intimately related to resonances for $|z| > \Delta$, since the total density of states satisfies a sum rule. Considerably more physical insight into the nature of the Maki bound states could be obtained by computing the local properties of the electron gas around the impurity spin. This has not been done yet using the SAN theory although Soda et al.[26] has considered this problem using a variational method.

REFERENCES

1. A. A. Abrikosov and L. P. Gor'kov, Zh. Eksperim. i Teor. Fiz. 39, 1781 (1960) [English transl: Soviet Phys. - JETP 12, 1243 (1961)].

2. K. Maki, in "Treatise on Superconductivity", edited by R. D. Parks (Marcel Dekker, Inc., N. Y., to be published).

3. T. Sugawara and H. Eguchi, J. Phys. Soc. Japan 21, 725 (1966).

4. G. Boato, G. Galinaro and C. Rizzuto, Phys. Rev. 148, 353 (1966).

5. L. P. Gor'kov and A. I. Rusinov, Zh. Eksperim. i Teor Fix 46, 1363 (1964) [English transl: Soviet Phys. - JETP 19, 922 (1964)].

6. M. D. Daybell and W. A. Steyert, Revs. Mod. Phys. 40, 380 (1968).

7. H. Suhl, in "Theory of Magnetism in Transition Metals", edited by W. Marshall (Academic Press, N. Y., 1967), p. 116.

8. A. A. Abrikosov, Physics 2, 5 (1965).

9. Y. Nagaoka, Phys. Rev. 138, 1112 (1965).

10. K. D. Schotte, Zeit. für Physik, 212, 467 (1968).

11. H. Keiter, Zeit. für Physik, (in press).

12. J. Zittartz and E. Müller-Hartmann, Zeit. für Physik 212, 380 (1968).

13. P. E. Bloomfield and D. R. Hamann, Phys. Rev. 164, 856 (1967).

14. K. Maki, Phys. Rev. 153, 428 (1967).

15. M. J. Zuckermann, Phys. Rev. 168, 390 (1968).

16. L. Dworin, Phys. Rev. 164, 818 (1967).

17. M. Kiwi and M. J. Zuckermann, Phys. Rev. 164, 548 (1967).

18. J. R. Schrieffer and P. A. Woolf, Phys. Rev. 149, 491 (1966).

19. J. Appelbaum, V. Celli and M. J. Zuckermann, Physics Letters 25A, 24 (1967).

20. Y. Nagaoka, J. Phys. Chem. Solids 27, 1139 (1966).

21. M. Fowler and K. Maki, Phys, Rev. 164, 484 (1967).

22. D. J. Kim, Phys. Rev. 149, 434 (1964); ibid. 167, 545 (1968).

23. S. Nakajima, Prog. Theor. Phys. 38, 23 (1967).

24. K. Yosida, Phys. Rev. 147, 223 (1966); M. A. Jensen and A. J. Heeger, Phys. Rev. Letters 18, 488 (1967).

25. H. U. Everts and B. N. Ganguly, Phys. Rev. (in press).

26. T. Soda, T. Matsuura and Y. Nagaoka, Prog. Theor. Phys. 38, 551 (1967).

27. D. R. Hamann, Phys. Rev. 158, 570 (1967).

28. S. D. Silverstein and C. B. Duke, Phys. Rev. 161, 456 (1967).

29. D. S. Falk and M. Fowler, Phys. Rev. 158, 567 (1967).

30. J. Kondo, Phys. Rev. 169, 437 (1968).

31. J. Heinrichs, Phys. Rev. 168, 451 (1968).

32. A. Griffin, Phys. Rev. Letters 15, 703 (1965).

33. K. Maki, private communication.

34. M. Fowler, Phys. Rev. 160, 463 (1967).

EXPERIMENTAL STUDIES
OF
SUPERCONDUCTORS WITH
MAGNETIC IMPURITIES

R. D. Parks

EXPERIMENTAL STUDIES
OF
SUPERCONDUCTORS WITH
MAGNETIC IMPURITIES

R. D. Parks
Department of Physics and Astronomy
University of Rochester
Rochester, New York

I. INTRODUCTION

To cover in any degree of completeness the
subject of superconductors with magnetic impurities
would require considerably more space than I am
entitled to use in these proceedings. Therefore, I
must exclude some material which is perhaps peri-
pheral to the central theme of this paper but which
properly belongs in a more thorough treatment of
the subject. For instance I shall delete the whole
area of physics which relates to the question of
whether a transition metal impurity exhibits a localized moment when dissolved in a metallic host.
The safest way to avoid this question is to limit the
discussion to rare earth impurities which are known
to exhibit well defined localized moments (since
there is little mixing between the 4f orbitals and
the conduction band). The discussion can be sim-
plified further by avoiding the discussion of spin

density fluctuations (paramagnons) which are believed to be important in the transition metals.[1] This can best be accomplished by restricting the discussion to non-transition-metal host materials. We are left then, hopefully, with the rather more puritanical problem of a simple, well understood metal containing well-defined localized moments. In order to further shrink the subject matter, I shall leave out all discussion of the Kondo effect and the possible coexistence of the Kondo-Nagaoka ground state and superconductivity.[2] An alternative reason for deleting this subject is the fact that the theory is preliminary and the experiments scant and not strongly convincing.

In order that we are not left with a situation which is too sterile, we shall allow the impurity spins to interact with each other, for sufficiently large spin concentrations, as a consequence of the Rudermann-Kittel-Kasuya-Yosida (RKKY) interaction.[3] This will take us into an area which has been somewhat prone to sensationalism in the past, viz. the problem of the coexistence of superconductivity and ferromagnetism (or other forms of magnetic order).

Since my task in this article is to review the experimental situation, the references I make to the theory will be brief and qualitative. The theory of superconductors with magnetic impurities will be covered in some depth by K. Bennemann in these proceedings.

II. IMPURITY SCATTERING AND ANDERSON'S CRITERION

Let us begin by taking a look at a situation in 1957 just after the publication of the BCS theory.[4] Although the essence of the understanding of superconductivity was contained in the BCS theory, some very fundamental questions were left unanswered by the BCS paper. One of these concerned the problem of superconductivity in (dirty) metals with very short mean free paths. It was known long before the BCS theory that if one doped a superconductor with chemical impurities (e.g., by adding a few percent Bi to In or a few percent In to Sn) this resulted in only minor changes in the thermodynamic properties of the superconductor. This at first sight seems odd for the following reason. In the BCS theory it was shown that if one calculates the phonon induced electron-electron interaction using time reversed plane wave states this leads to a pairwise binding of the electrons. Such pairs we shall refer to as Cooper pairs. The binding energy Δ of the pairs at $T = 0°K$ is $1.75 \, kT_c$ and their lifetime of order $\hbar/\Delta$ or about 10^{-12} sec for a typical superconductor.[4] Now, in an alloy such as In-2% Bi the mean free path is of the order of 100 Å, which implies that the lifetime of the momentum eigenstates is of the order of 10^{-14} sec corresponding to an energy uncertainty of the states which is roughly 100 times the binding energy of a Cooper pair. In the case of amorphous films evaporated onto cryogenic substrates the mean free path can be as small as 1 Å which corresponds to an energy uncertainty of the momentum eigenstates which is greater even than the Debye frequency, yet the superconducting state (zero field) thermodynamic properties of such systems are little changed from those of the bulk material.

Although (non-magnetic) chemical impurities have little effect on the zero field thermodynamic properties of a superconductor, the story with magnetic impurities is quite different as was first shown by Matthias and coworkers[5] in 1958. Shown in Fig. 1 are the results from Ref. 2 for the dependence of T_c of La on the concentration of dissolved Gd. The depression of T_c with Gd concentration is very rapid— and extrapolation of the results suggests that a Gd concentration of the order of one percent leads to the complete extinction of superconductivity at T = $0°$ K.

How can we reconcile the vast difference between the effect of non-magnetic and magnetic impurities on superconductivity? Anderson[6] produced the answer not long after the 1958 paper of Matthias and coworkers. Anderson suggested that the proper approach in the treatment of superconductivity in the presence of impurity scattering is the following. One first solves (in principle) the impurity scattering problem, i.e. one finds the eigenfunctions $\phi'_{n\sigma}$ which diagonalize the Hamiltonian which includes the impurity scattering potential U. One then calculates the phonon induced electron-electron interaction not between time reversed plane wave states as per BCS but between the $\phi_{n\sigma}$'s and $\phi_{n\sigma}$'s, where $\phi'_{n\sigma} = K\phi_{n\sigma}$ K being the time reversal operator which maps r into r, p into -p and s into -s (r, p and s are the spatial, momentum and spin coordinates respectively). Anderson then showed that if $\phi'_{n\sigma}$ is energetically degenerate with $\phi_{n\sigma}$ with respect to U that the BCS interaction

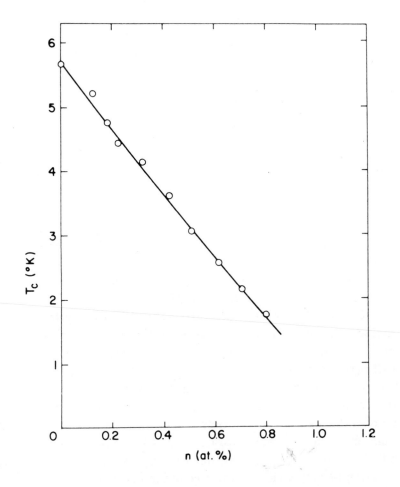

Fig. 1. Dependence of T_c of $La_{1-x}Gd_x$ on concentration of Gd (from Ref. 5).

calculated in the new representation reduces to a form which is identical to the BCS interaction between time reversed plane wave states. By Kramer's theory $\phi'_{n\sigma}$ and $\phi_{n\sigma}$ are energetically degenerate with respect to U only if K commutes with U, i.e., $[K, U] = 0$. If $[K, U] \neq 0$ the effective electron-electron interaction between the states $\phi_{n\sigma}$ and $\phi'_{n\sigma}$ does not reduce to the BCS form, but gives rise instead to an effective repulsive interaction between these states which opposes the formation of Cooper pairs. The above commutation criterion provides a convenient method for determining whether a particular perturbation is detremental to superconductivity (i.e., produces pair breaking effects). In the case of magnetic scattering centers, obviously $[K, U] \neq 0$ since the time reversed states see unequal scattering cross sections. The same is true of the case of a superconductor in contact with a normal metal, where, clearly, time reversed states see different scattering potentials in the interface region. Later we shall encounter other examples of pair breaking situations.

Early attempts to generalize the BCS theory to include the effects of paramagnetic impurities were based on ordinary perturbation theory wherein the BCS ground state and excited states were used as the unperturbed wave functions. An example of this was the paper of Suhl and Matthias [7] which predicted a convex T_c vs n curve (n being the concentration of magnetic impurities) with $dT_c/dn \to 0$ as $n \to 0$ and $dT_c/dn \to \infty$ as $T_c \to 0$, and that the superconducting-to-normal transition in the presence of magnetic impurities would be first order. Shortly following these predictions specific heat measurements by Muller and Pisi [8] and critical field measurement by

the author[9] indicated that the zero field transition
was second order, contrary to the predictions of
the calculations based on ordinary perturbation
theory.

III. ABRIKOSOV-GOR'KOV THEORY

The failing of the ordinary perturbation theory
approach to the magnetic impurity problem results
from the fact that since the superconducting order
parameter is changed considerably by the presence
of magnetic impurities, it is necessary to treat
both the phonon induced electron-electron interaction
and the electron-impurity interaction on the same
footing. Abrikosov and Gor'kov[10] took this approach,
employing Green's function techniques which allows
one to handily consider the simutaneous response of
the system to both interactions. The details of the
Abrikosov Gor'kov (AG) theory will be given in
Bennemann's chapter, so I shall merely summarize
here the assumptions and predictions of the theory.
The approximations in the AG calculation were the
following:
    1. The order parameter is assumed to be
spatially constant. This requires that the spin impurities be evenly (randomly) distributed on the
host's lattice.
    2. The impurity spins are assumed to be un-
polarized and uncorrelated. This implies the absence
of magnetic ordering effects and spin fluctuations
which involve more than one impurity spin.
    3. The effect of the impurities on the Green's
function is treated only in the first Born approximation.

The first order correction to the Green's function vanishes because of requirement 2, and in second order only double scattering from the same impurity is considered.

The theory predicts that the zero field super-conducting-normal transition is second order, and that the zero field coexistence curve which separates the normal and superconducting phases is given by the simple relation,

$$\ln \frac{T_c}{T_{co}} + \psi \left(\tfrac{1}{2} + \rho \right) - \psi \left(\tfrac{1}{2} \right) = 0$$

with   (1)

$$\rho = \frac{1}{2\pi T_c \tau_{ex}} \text{ and } (\tau_{ex})^{-1} = n\pi N(0) J_{ex}^2 S(S+1),$$

where $\psi(z)$ is the digamma function, T_c and T_{co} are the transition temperatures in the presence of and absence of magentic impurities respectively, τ_{ex} is the scattering time associated with the exchange scattering [of strength J_{ex}] from the magnetic impurities, n is the density of magnetic impurities, $N(0)$ the density of states at the fermi energy for both spins and S the total spin of the impurity. If the spin impurity has non-zero orbital momentum and complete spin orbit coupling obtains, the factor $S(S+1)$ must be replaced by $(\mathbf{J \cdot S})^2/J(J+1)$, since the conduction electrons see only the time averaged projection of $\mathbf{S}$ on $\mathbf{J}$ (the total angular momentum). Equation (1) can be cast into the following handy form,

$$\ln \frac{T_c}{T_{co}} + \psi \left(\tfrac{1}{2} + 0.14 \frac{T_{co}}{T_c} \frac{\alpha}{\alpha_{cr}} \right) - \psi \left(\tfrac{1}{2} \right), \quad (2)$$

where α/α_{cr} is the normalized pair breaking parameter which in the present case is identical to n/n_{cr} (n_{cr} being the concentration of magnetic impurities required to depress T_c to zero). A plot of Eq. (2) is given in Fig. 2. As we shall see later Eq. (2) has far wider application (to various pair breaking situations) than that discussed in the present context. Equation (1) or (2) predicts an initial linear dependence of T_c on n as observed by Matthias and co-workers,[5] but an infinite slope of dT_c/dn in the limit $n \to n_{cr}$.

In addition to predicting the shape of the zero field coexistence curves which corresponds to the limit $\Delta \to 0$ where Δ is the (superconducting) order parameter, the AG theory treats the situation for finite Δ. A prediction which caused much excitement and some disbelief concerns the excitation spectrum of such a superconductor. Shown in Fig. 3 are the predicted density of states curves corresponding to $T = 0\,°K$ for different values of the pairbreaking parameter α (from Skalski et al.[11]). For $\alpha = 0$, one has the BCS curve which is divergent at $\epsilon - \epsilon_f = \Delta$; for the value of α corresponding to point 1 (α_1) there is a slight distortion of the density of states curve, for α_2 the distortion is even greater, for α_4 the gap in the spectrum disappears, and for α_6 the density of states curve differs little from that of the normal state despite the fact that the resistance of the superconductor is presumably zero and the condensation energy finite.

The first really convincing verification the AG theory was provided by the beautiful electron tunneling experiments of Woolf and Reif.[12] The experiments were carried out in a He^3 calorimeter with

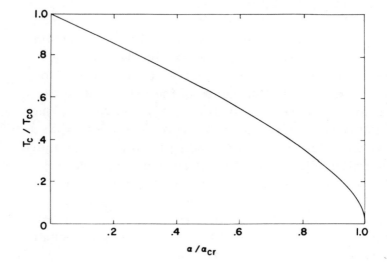

Fig. 2. Universal pair breaking curve in terms of
reduced temperature T_c/T_{co} and reduced pair breaking parameter α/α_{cr}.

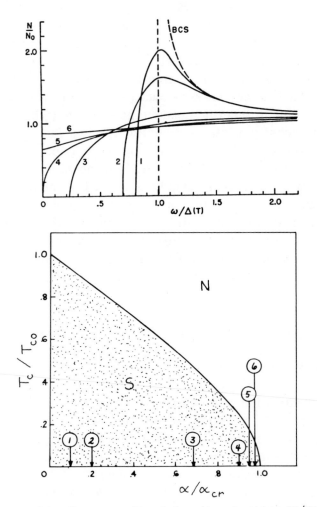

Fig. 3. (Top) Normalized density of states N/N_O vs. normalized energy $w/ \Delta(t)$ curves ($T = 0°K$) corresponding to different values of the pair breaking parameter α/α_{cr} (from below). The zero of the energy axis is the Fermi energy (from Ref. 11).

thin film samples which were evaporated onto cryogenic substrates. Various systems were studied
(e.g., $Pb_{1-x}Gd_x$, $In_{1-x}Fe_x$, $Pb_{1-x}Mn_x$) all of which
exhibited at least qualitatively the spilling over of
states into the gap as indicated in Fig. 3. The best
quantitative agreement was obtained with the Pb_{1-x}
Gd_x system. Tunneling conductance curves (which
give the density of states directly) for two Pb_{1-x}
Gd_x samples are shown in Fig. 4 to be in good agreement with the curves calculated from the AG theory.

    Another impressive study consisted of the specific
heat experiments of Finnemore et al.[13] on bulk La_{1-x}
Gd_x. The AG theory predicts a dimunition of the jump
in the specific heat at T_c with increasing spin impurity
concentration; this is shown in Fig. 5 (from Ref. 11)
along with the data points of Finnemore et al.

IV. EFFECTS OF MAGNETIC ORDERING

A. Anomalous coexistence curves.

    An extension of the early measurements of
Matthias et al.[5] on $La_{1-x}Gd_x$ by Hein and coworkers[1]
to lower temperatures revealed the phase diagram
in Fig. 6. For higher Gd concentrations the data
exhibits an anomalous departure from the AG curve
which was determined by fitting the theory [Eq. (2)]
to the data in the linear portion of the curve. Shown
also in Fig. 6 is a plot of T_m vs n, where T_m denotes the onset of magnetic ordering as determined
from magnetic susceptibility measurements made
in the normal state. The magnetic ordering was
assumed to be ferromagnetic but subsequent

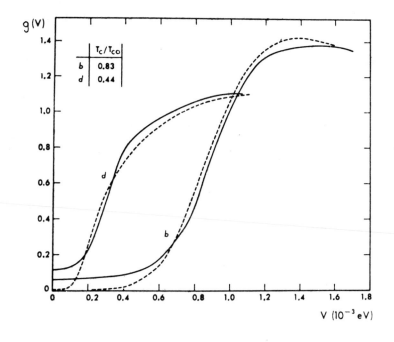

Fig. 4. Density of states curves from the tunneling
data of Woolf and Reif (Ref. 12) for $Pb_{1-x}Gd_x$ with 0.61
at % Gd (sample b) and $Pb_{1-x}Gd_x$ with 2.02 at % Gd
(sample d) compared with (dashed line) prediction of
AG theory.

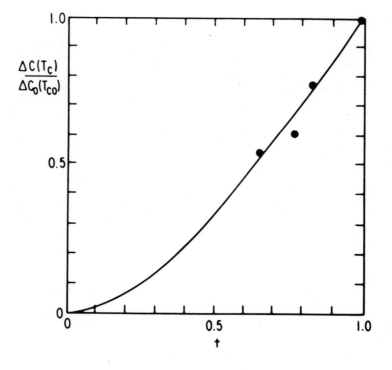

Fig. 5. Jump in specific heat at T_c as a function of
$t = T_c/T_{co}$. Solid circles are experimental points
from Ref. 13; the curve is calculated from AG theory
(Ref. 11).

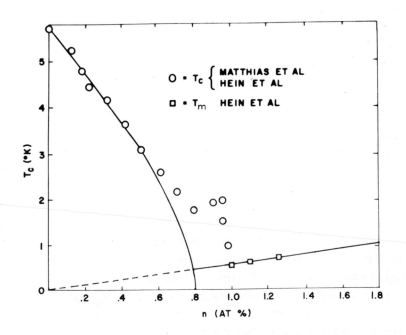

Fig. 6. Circles: T_c of $La_{1-x}Gd_x$ vs. Gd concentration. (from Refs. 4 and 14). Squares: T_m (temperature of susceptibility maximum) vs. Gd concentration (from Ref. 14). Solid curve is the AG pair breaking curve.

experiments by Finnemore et al.[15] on carefully prepared samples seemed to refute this. Finnemore et
al. found enhanced susceptibilities and peaks in the
susceptibility vs. temperature of $La_{1-x}Gd_x$, the
temperatures of the peaks agreeing with the values
of T_m reported by Hein et al. However, the measured remanence for $T < T_m$ was found to be neg-
ligibly small and the susceptibility peaks were found
to be sensitive to small magnetic fields, being depressed to lower temperatures in the presence of
field. This behavior is certainly not characteristic
of a system with long range ferromagnetic order.
We shall return to the question of the nature of
magnetic order in dilute magnetic alloys in subsequent discussions.

The phase diagram shown in Fig. 6 aroused
considerable interest in the question of the coexistence of superconductivity and ferromagnetism (or
other types of magnetic order).

B. Specific heat studies

In order to demonstrate that both superconductivity and ordered magnetism could coexist on a
microscopic scale, Phillips and Matthias [16] made
specific heat measurements on the $La_{1-x}Gd_x$ and
$Y_{1-x}Gd_xOs_2$ systems. In both systems large but
broad maxima were observed in the specific heat
which were associated with the decrease in entropy
corresponding the onset magnetic order, (which
should be $xRln(2S+1)$ if the magnetic ordering is
complete). In the $Y_{1-x}Gd_xOs_2$ system only about
50% of the total magnetic entropy was accounted for
whereas in the $La_{1-x}Gd_x$ system (with x = 0.007)

the excess specific heat corresponded to the expected
decrease in entropy if the magnetic ordering was
complete. Finnemore et al[13] later corraborated
this result. Phillips and Matthias attempted to determine whether superconductivity extended throughout
the sample in the presence of magnetic order by
measuring the specific heat in the presence and absence of a magnetic field large enough to quench the
superconductivity. The entropy differences between
the normal and superconducting states determined
in this way were of the right order of magnitude for
the $La_{.993}Gd_{.007}$ system. However, because of the
lack of knowledge about the nature of the ordered
magnetism in $La_{1-x}Gd_x$ as discussed above, one cannot be certain that the change in entropy upon application of a magnetic field can be attributed solely to the
entropy difference between the superconducting and
normal states. The application of a magnetic field
produces a decrease in entropy in a paramagnetic
system, an increase in entropy in an antiferromagnetic system and essentially no change in entropy
in a ferromagnetic system with long range order. As
will be discussed later, it is doubtful that the type
of magnetic order in $La_{1-x}Gd_x$ and other dilute
magnetic alloys falls into any of these simple categories.

C. The $InLa_{3-x}Gd_x$ system

    In view of the anomalous features of the La_{1-x}
Gd_x coexistence curve (Fig. 6) the need was clearly
evident for thorough experimental studies of other
systems. Crow and Parks [17] undertook such a study
of the (intermetallic) $InLa_{3-x}Gd_x$ system. This
system was chosen because of its high T_c, which is

convenient in terms of carrying out experiments at small reduced temperatures, and the expectation that the system would exhibit homogeneous, monophase, solid solutions at least for small Gd concentrations, thereby allowing one to avoid the two-crystal phase-problem inherent in the $La_{1-x}Gd_x$ studies.[15] The zero field coexistence curve for $InLa_{3-x}Gd_x$ is shown in Fig. 7. As with the $La_{1-x}Gd_x$ system an anomalous departure from the AG curve is observed for higher Gd concentrations; however, the results are qualitatively different from those of the $La_{1-x}Gd_x$ system in that the values of T_c are anomalously small rather than anomalously large. Shown also in the figure is a plot of T_m vs n, the T_m's being the temperatures associated with peaks in the measured susceptibilities (which were interpreted as reflecting the onset of magnetic ordering). The behavior of the $InLa_{3-x}Gd_x$ and $La_{1-x}Gd_x$ systems are compared in the normalized plots of Fig. 8.

D. Bennemann theory

Shortly after the publication of the $InLa_{3-x}Gd_x$ results, Bennemann[18] explained how the onset of magnetic order could lead to either of the two types of anomalous behavior shown in Fig. 8. The qualitative essence of his explanation is the following. To simplify the discussion let us first assume that the type of magnetic order is long range ferromagnetism. The onset of ferromagnetism leads to the following effects:

1. A decrease in the spin impurity scattering cross-section seen by the conduction electrons. The total scattering cross-section is proportional to

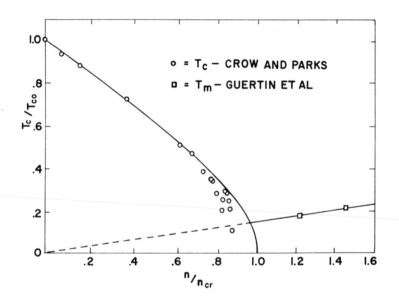

Fig. 7. Circles: T_c/T_{co} of $InLa_{3-x}Gd_x$ vs. normalized Gd concentration, n_{cr} being critical concentration (from Ref. 17). Squares: T_m/T_{co} (where T_m is temperature of susceptibility maximum) vs. Gd concentration (from Ref. 21).

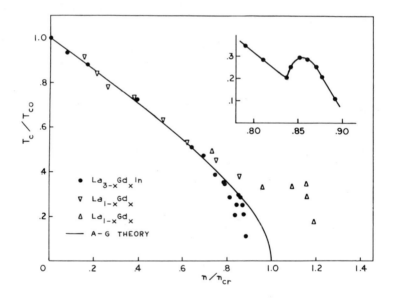

Fig. 8. Summary of results for T_c/T_{co} vs. n/n_{cr} experiments on $La_{1-x}Gd_x$ and $InLa_{3-x}$ systems (from Figs. 6 and 7). Region of anomaly in $InLa_{3-x}Gd_x$ curve is magnified in inset.

$\langle \mathbf{S \cdot S} \rangle$, where

$$\langle \mathbf{S \cdot S} \rangle = \langle S_z^2 \rangle + \langle S_+ S_- \rangle .$$

The non-spin-flip scattering cross section is proportional to $\langle S_z^2 \rangle$ and the spin flip scattering cross section is proportional to $\langle S_+ S_- \rangle$. In the paramagnetic limit, $\mu H_{eff}/kT \ll 1$, where μ is the moment of the magnetic impurity and H_{eff} the effective field acting on the impurity, $\langle S_z^2 \rangle$ and $\langle S_+ S_- \rangle$ have the values $S(S+1)/3$ and $2S(S+1)/3$ respectively. In the presence of strong internal fields ($\mu H_{eff}/kT \gg 1$) (e.g., due to ferromagnetism) the spin-flip scattering is quenched because of the Zeeman splitting of the impurity spin levels, coupled with the fact that there is a paucity of conduction electrons in the Fermi distribution which are allowed to change their energies by $\mu H_{eff} \gg kT$. The asymptotic values of $\langle S_z^2 \rangle$ and $\langle S_+ S_- \rangle$ in the limit $\mu H_{eff} \gg kT$ are S^2 and zero respectively. The ratio of the total scattering cross sections in the two extreme limits is $(S+1)/S$, corresponding to the same ratio of n_{cr} in the two limits.

2. The appearance of polarization in the electron gas (Pauli paramagnetism effects). This results from the exchange coupling of the conduction electrons to the aligned impurity spins and is detrimental to superconductivity since there is less phase space in a polarized electron gas for the construction of the BCS state with time reversed pairs. Another way of looking at this effect is to write down the magnetic dependent part of the free energies of the superconducting and normal states in the presence of H_{eff}. They are

$$F_s{}^M = - \chi_p{}^s H_{eff}{}^2$$

$$F_n{}^M = -\chi_p{}^n H_{eff}{}^2 \tag{4}$$

respectively, where $\chi_p{}^s$ is the Pauli susceptibility in the superconducting state and $\chi_p{}^n$ the Pauli susceptibility in the normal state. Now since

$$(\chi_p{}^n - \chi_p{}^s)$$

is a positive quantity, the relation

$$F_n{}^M < F_s{}^M$$

always holds. When

$$(F_s{}^M - F_n{}^M)$$

exceeds the (BCS) condensation energy the sample will revert to the normal state.

3. <u>But spin orbit scattering moderates effect #2.</u> As shown first by Ferrell [19] and Anderson [20] spin orbit scattering strongly affects $\chi_p{}^s$; in the limit of strong spin orbit scattering

$$\chi_p{}^s \rightarrow \chi_p{}^n,$$

which corresponds to

$$F_s{}^M - F_n{}^M \rightarrow 0.$$

Spin orbit scattering therefore reduces the detrimental effects of Pauli paramagnetism to the superconducting state.

These various effects are illustrated in Fig. 9. In (a) one has the expected T_c vs n behavior if (1) (the decrease in spin flip scattering) is the only effect considered; (this would be appropriate to the case of antiferromagnetic ordering) in (b) only (2) (Pauli paramagnetism) is considered. One can obtain curves of the type shown in (c) by combining (1), (2) and (3), prescribing some ad hoc distribution of internal field H_{eff} and temperature dependence of these fields, and prescribing some value for the spin orbit scattering cross section. Using the approach described in (c) Bennemann obtained the theoretical curves shown in Figs. 10 and 11 which are in qualitative accord with the experimental results.

The fact that the data points for $InLa_{3-x}Gd_x$ fall short of the AG curve for higher Gd concentrations implies that Pauli ferromagnetism effects are important which in turn implies that ferromagnetism is present and that the characteristic dimension of the ferromagnetic domains ξ_M is of the order or larger than the superconducting coherence length ξ_o. If $\xi_M \ll \xi_o$ the BCS interaction averages over the various polarization directions and is not decreased from its value in the paramagnetic limit. From critical field and magnetization studies, which will be discussed below, it has been determined that the value of ξ_o for $InLa_3$ is of the order of 70 Å. Thus from the superconducting studies of $InLa_{3-x}Gd_x$ [Fig. 11] we can say that the system exhibits a kind of ferromagnetic state in which the size of the ferromagnetic domains is of the order of at least 70 Å. This is considerably more than we can say about the nature of the ordered magnetism from measurements made in the normal state, which are discussed below.

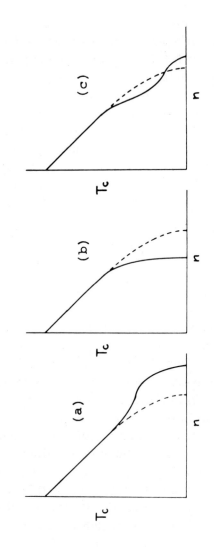

Fig. 9. Predicted, schematic T_c vs. n curves for various situations (see text). The dashed curve is AG result.

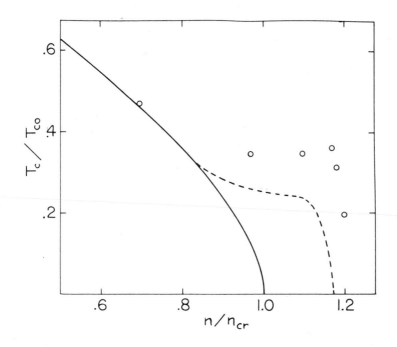

Fig. 10. Experimental results for $La_{1-x}Gd_x$ system
(Refs. 5 and 14) compared with Bennemann's theory
(dashed line) and AG theory (solid line).

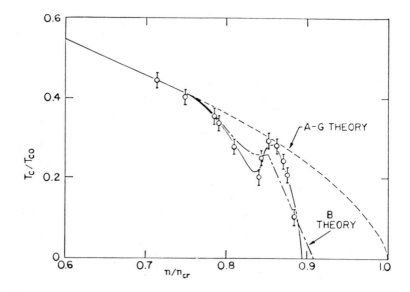

Fig. 11. Experimental results for InLa$_{3-x}$Gd$_x$ system (Ref. 17) compared with the theories of Bennemann (B) and Abrikosov-Gor'kov (A-G).

MAGNETIC IMPURITIES 651

E. Normal state studies

   The temperature dependence of the magnetic
susceptibilities χ of various $InLa_{3-x}Gd_x$ samples
(measured by Guertin, Crow and Parks[21]) are shown
in Fig. 12. The χ vs. T. curves exhibit peaks not
unlike the behavior found in the $La_{1-x}Gd_x$ system.[15, 22]
The peaks reflect presumably the onset of magnetic
order. The fact that the peaks are broad suggest
that the magnetic order sets in gradually rather than
abruptly with decreasing temperature. The fact that
the susceptibilities are enormous compared to the
calculated Brillouin values in the vicinity of the peak
and at higher temperatures suggests that at least
short range ferromagnetic ordering effects are important in this temperature range. Measurements
at $1.2°K$ showed that the 2.61% and 3.00% samples
had no remanence when demagnetized from a 1000
g field and that the 4.26% sample had 2% saturation
remanence. The lack of remanence seems to imply
the lack of long range ferromagnetic order. These
results are not inconsistent with the conclusions
drawn from the T_c vs n studies discussed above,
viz. that there are ferromagnetic correlations over
distances of the order or larger than ~ 70 A.
   The magnetic susceptibility of the $La_{1-x}Gd_x$
system is qualitatively similar[15, 22] except that the
ratio χ/χ_B is not as large as observed for the
$InLa_3Gd_x$ system (the data for $La_{0.95}Gd_{0.05}$ are
shown in Fig. 12). The fact that the zero field
coexistence curves for $La_{1-x}Gd_x$ and $InLa_{3-x}Gd_x$
[Fig. 8] are quite dissimilar does not preclude the
possibility that the nature of the magnetic ordering
is the same in both systems, the difference in be-

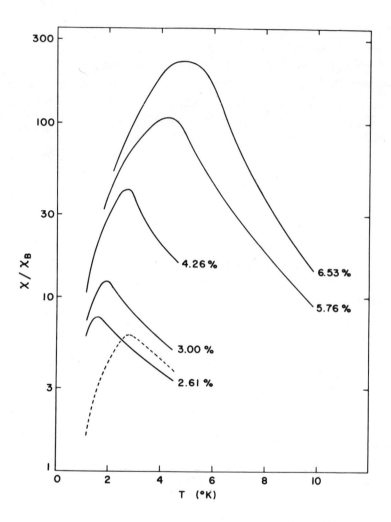

Fig. 12. Normalized magnetic susceptibility χ/χ_B vs. T for various concentrations (at %) of Gd, where χ_B is calculated Brillouin susceptibility. Solid curves are for $InLa_{3-x}Gd_x$, dashed curve is for $La_{1-x}Gd_x$ (from Ref. 21).

havior being explained entirely in terms of the difference in the BCS coherence lengths in the two systems. The coherence length of La, obtained by using
the formula, [23]

$$\xi_0^{\,2} = \phi_0/2\pi H_{c2}(0)$$

(where ϕ_0 is the flux quantum and H_{c2} (0) the upper
critical magnetic field) and the value H_{c2} (0) $\approx$ 3000
gauss from the critical field studies of Finnemore
et al.[13], is approximately 320 Å compared to 70 Å
for $InLa_{3-x}Gd_x$. If then the characteristic range of
ferromagnetic coherence is of the order of say 50 Å,
this would lead to large Pauli paramagnetism effects
in the $InLa_{3-x}Gd_x$ system but negligible effects in the
$La_{1-x}Gd_x$ system and the qualitative differences in
the coexistence curves shown in Fig. 8 could be explained.

F. Klein-Brout-Marshall Theory

The apparent lack of long range magnetic order
in the dilute La-rare earth systems is consistent
with the predictions of the Klein-Brout-Marshall[24-27]
(KBM) statistical approach to the problem of dilute
magnetic alloys. One central feature of this approach
is that the effective field produced by the Ruderman-
Kittel interaction between impurity spins has a continuous probability function with the distribution
curve peaking at non-zero values of the field at low
temperature, but the theory predicts no sharp phase
transition. The KBM theory does predict a peak in
the magnetic susceptibility [24] at a temperature
T_{max} which scales linearly with impurity concentration. But the model also predicts that the height of

the peak should be independent of the concentration
and smaller than the Brillouin value, in disagreement with the results in Fig. 12. Another feature
of the model which is most relevant to the present
discussion is that the correlation length R_c (which
is probably related to the quantity ξ_M discussed
earlier) decreases with increasing concentration,
varying as $R_c \sim 0.5 \ d/n^{1/3}$, where d is the lattice
constant and n the fraction of impurities. This
effect (if it persists in an extension of the KBM
model to take into account higher order, ferromagnetic spin-spin terms) might enter in the explanation of the anomalous bump in the coexistence
curve of $InLa_{3-x}Gd_x$ (Fig. 8). If the range of ferromagnetic order is decreasing with increasing Gd
concentrations, this could lead to a decrease in the
Pauli paramagnetism effects and a concomitant increase in T_c.

The weakness of the KBM theory lies in the
cutting off of the cluster expansion of the partition
function at the two-spin correlation term. While
this procedure might be valid for extremely small
impurity concentrations ($n \ll 1\%$), it is expected
that higher order spin-spin correlations will be
important for larger impurity concentrations.
Liu[28] has attempted to extend the KBM theory to
higher concentrations, by retaining the philosophy
of the KBM approach but by making the ad hoc assumption that the most probable value of the effective field shifts to lower values with decreasing
temperature in analogy with a similar prediction
of the Weiss molecular field theory. Liu's model
leads to a predicted magnetic susceptibility behavior
which is qualitatively similar to that observed in the
$La_{1-x}Gd_x$ and $InLa_{3-x}Gd_x$ systems.

G. Further discussion of coexistence curves

Let us return for the moment to the s-n coexistence curves of the $La_{1-x}Gd_x$ and $InLa_{3-x}Gd_x$ systems (Figs. 6 and 7). Note that the departure of the data from the AG curve occurs at temperatures considerably higher than the temperature of magnetic ordering determined from the extrapolated line of susceptibility maxima. Recent work[29] on the $Th_{1-x}Er_x$ system sheds some light on this problem. The coexistence curve of $Th_{1-x}Er_x$ system is shown schematically in Fig. 13 together with the line of susceptibility maxima. The susceptibility maxima observed in the $Th_{1-x}Er_x$ system for values of x in the vicinity of the critical concentrations differ from these reported above for the $InLa_{3-x}Gd_x$ and $La_{1-x}Gd_x$ systems in that the peaks are much sharper and the susceptibility at the peak is smaller than the Brillouin value suggesting perhaps the onset of antiferromagnetism instead of some more complicated, non-descript type of magnetic ordering. Shown also in Fig. 13 is the line of T_d's (where T_d is the temperature at which the magnetic susceptibility departs from the Brillouin susceptibility), taken from Fig. 14. The line of T_d's intersects the point on the coexistence curve where anomalous behavior sets in. This denotes presumably the temperature at which long wavelength spin fluctuations start to become important or where a large scale inhomogeneity begins to appear in the (static) magnetic field distributions.

Another point which is most relevant to the discussion of the coexistence of ordered magnetism and superconductivity is the one made by Gor'kov

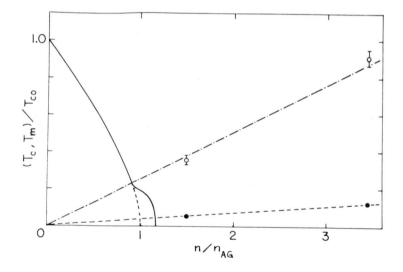

Fig. 13. Solid curve: Schematic curve of T_c/T_{co} vs. n/n_{AG} for $Th_{1-x}Er_x$ (from Ref. 29) where n_{AG} is critical concentration predicted by AG theory; Solid circles: T_m/T_{co} vs. n/n_{AG}, where T_m is the temperature of susceptibility maximum; Open circles: T_d/T_{co} vs. n/n_{AG}, where T_d is temperature at which χ departs from Curie law behavior (taken from Fig. 14).

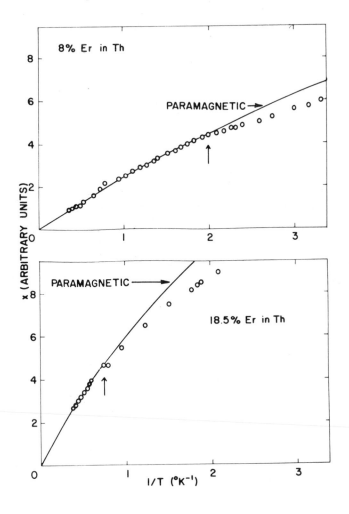

Fig. 14. Magnetic susceptibility (proportional to x)
vs. 1/T for two $Th_{1-x}Er_x$ alloys. Arrows denote departure from Curie law behavior. The curvature of
the (paramagnetic) lines reflects the inclusion of
sample shape demagnetization corrections.

and Rusinov[30] concerning the effect of superconductivity on the RKKY interaction. Their qualitative
prediction is illustrated in the phase diagram in Fig.
15 which denotes the superconducting region S, the
paramagnetic region P, the magnetically ordered
region M and the regions of coexistence of superconductivity and magnetism (C and C'). The point
made by Gor'kov and Rusinov is that when the system
becomes superconducting, there is a decrease in the
Pauli susceptibility χ_p and hence a decrease in the
RKKY interaction (leading to a decrease in the magnetic ordering temperature T_m) since the interaction is directly proportional to χ_p. This would
lead to the region of coexistence C' instead of the
region C+C' defined by the extrapolation of the P-M
coexistence line to n = 0. However, since the presence
of spin-orbit scattering leads to an increase of χ_p
in the superconducting state, for sufficiently strong
spin orbit scattering the curve separating regions
C and C' would straighten and move to the position
of the dashed line. While Gor'kov and Rusinov discussed only ferromagnetism, it is clear that the
same arguments would apply to any type of magnetic
order produced by the Rudermann-Kittel interaction.
This effect (the depression of T_m as a result of
superconductivity) has not yet been observed. The
specific heat peaks, associated with the onset of
magnetic ordering in the superconducting state, in
the studies by Phillips and Matthias [16] and Finnemore et al[13] were too broad to permit an accurate
determination of T_m.

Recently several systems have been discovered
for which the ratio T_m/n is small enough to allow
one to measure the AG coexistence curve over a

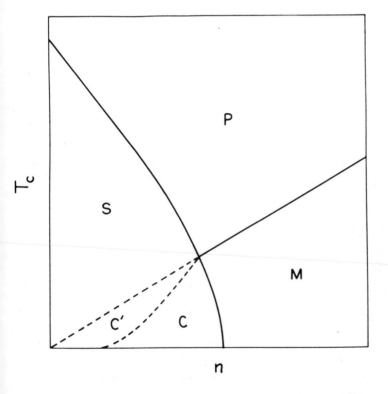

Fig. 15. Phase diagram exhibiting superconducting
D, paramagnetic P, magnetically ordered M, and
S-M coexistence (C and C') phases (see text).

large range of impurity concentrations with no interference from magnetic ordering effects. The coexistence curve for $Al_2La_{1-x}Gd_x$ [Fig. 16] is found to
be in excellent agreement with the AG curve even
for Gd concentrations quite close to the critical concentration.[31] Similar results have been found for
the $Th_{1-x}Gd_x$ system.[29]

H. Cryptoferromagnetism

An interesting suggestion which deserves comment
is the "cryptoferromagnetic" state proposed by Anderson and Suhl.[32] The idea is that the total energy of
a system coexisting in the ferromagnetic and superconducting states can be lowered if the ferromagnetic
state adjusts itself to form ferromagnetic domains
which are smaller than the superconducting coherence
length and organized in a non-random way which
would allow the BCS pairing between time reversed
states to proceed unhindered by Pauli paramagnetism
effects. It was assumed that the spectral function
$S(q)$ of the impurity spins would be peaked at a q
value corresponding to the reciprocal ferromagnetic
domain length. Such a strictly periodic spin dependent potential would lead to a reduction on the spin
scattering of the conduction electrons (as discussed
more recently by Bennemann[18]) and therefore a
lowering in energy of the superconducting-crypto-
ferromagnetic state with respect to the super-
conducting-paramagnetic state.

There is no evidence yet for the cryptoferromagnetic state. In fact the phase diagram for
$InLa_{3-x}Gd_x$ (Fig. 1) might be taken as evidence
against the formation of such a state since Anderson

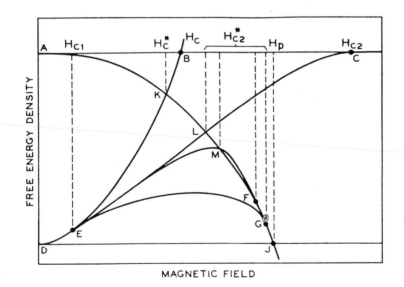

Fig. 16. Schematic free energy diagram indicating field response in different superconducting regimes (see text).

Table 1. Systems used in critical magnetic field studies.

System		T_C of pure matrix	Upper critical field of pure matrix at $T=0°K$	Field induced state
$Th_{1-x}Gd_x$	0.5	1.39°K	159 gauss	Meissner state
$(Th-5\%La)_{1-x}Er_x$	4	1.53°K	900 gauss	Vortex state
$InLa_{3-x}Gd_x$	$\gtrsim 20$	9.2°K	70,000 gauss	Vortex state + exchange enhanced conduction electron polarization (Pauli paramagnetism)

and Suhl predict an increase rather than a decrease in T_c with the onset of magnetic order. On the other hand perhaps the anomalous bump in the $InLa_{3-x}Gd_x$ coexistence curve denotes the onset of the crypto-ferromagnetic state. The formation of such a state in a very dilute magnetic alloy would seem to be inconsistent with the result from the Klein-Brout-Marshall theory that in such systems the spin correlation lengths are extremely short and the magnetic spectral functions are very broad and unstructured. The most suitable systems to use when searching for the Anderson-Suhl state would be ones in which the s-f (or s-d) exchange interaction is quite small which means that larger spin impurity concentrations could be used. In such systems higher order spin-spin interactions would be important and it would be possible to obtain the long range spin correlations required in the Anderson-Suhl model. The ideal experiment would be one which could measure the spectral function of the impurity spins, e.g., a neutron scattering experiment.

V. EFFECTS OF APPLIED MAGNETIC FIELD

A. Introduction

Reasonably thorough critical magnetic field studies have been made of the three representative systems whose properties are tabulated in Table 1. As evident from the table the systems differ widely in their properties and in their response to an applied magnetic field. Before discussing the behavior of these particular systems I shall review briefly

the various mechanisms which can come into play
when a superconductor is subjected to a magnetic
field. For this purpose it is convenient to refer to
the schematic free energy diagram in Fig. 16 due
to Werthamer et al.[33] The horizontal lines AC and
DJ represent the free energies in the normal and
superconducting states respectively in the absence
of magnetic field. If an ordinary Type I superconductor (e.g. pure Sn, In, Th, etc.) is subjected to
a magnetic field, it will exhibit a Meissner effect
(diamagnetic response) and the free energy will increase with increasing field, following the curve
DEKB, and will suffer a first-order (F.O) phase
transition to the normal state at point B. If one includes Pauli spin paramagnetism effects in the normal state (see discussion in Section IV.C.) it will
undergo a F.O. S-n transition at point K. A type II
superconductor, one in which the Ginzburg-Landau
parameter $\kappa \sim \lambda/\xi$ (where λ is the penetration depth
and ξ the coherence length) is larger than $1/\sqrt{2}$, behaves differently in that it enters the vortex state
at some field H_{c1} and superconductivity persists up
to a field H_{c2} which is given by $H_{c2} = \sqrt{2}\kappa H_{cb}$ (H_{cb}
being the thermodynamic critical field.). The
schematic free energy curve appropriate to a type
II superconductor is DELC. At point C there is a
second order (S.O) phase transition to the normal
state. If again one includes the spin paramagnetism
in the normal state, this would lead to a F.O., s-n
transition at L. To make the discussion complete
we note (as discussed in the Section IV.C.) that the
presence of spin-orbit scattering leads to an increase
in the spin susceptibility in the superconducting state
(χ_p^S). In addition Fulde and Maki[34] have shown that

$\chi_p{}^S$ is also a function of the applied magnetic field (if the field produces pair-breaking effects as in the vortex state), increasing with increasing field. Taking these two facts into account one can obtain curves such as DEMF or DEGJ. Whether the transition is F.O. as at M or S.O. as at G depends upon the value of the spin orbit scattering time and other parameters.

Let us return now to Table 1 and discuss first the case of $Th_{1-x}Gd_x$ which is a Type I superconductor, i.e., it undergoes a first order phase transition to the normal state at the critical magnetic field. Decker et al.[35] have performed very careful measurements of the critical magnetic field H_c of this system. The results shown in Fig. 17, are in excellent agreement with the behavior calculated by Skalski et al.[11] from the Abrikosov-Gor'kov theory. Although the predicted departure from the BCS theory is small, the measurements were sufficiently accurate to allow one to clearly distinguish the difference between the temperature dependences of H_c predicted by the BCS and AG theories. Before discussing the critical field behavior of the $(Th-5\%La)_{1-x}Er_x$ and $InLa_{3-x}Gd_x$ systems it would be useful and relevant to discuss briefly the various possible depairing phenomena in superconductors and in particular, multiple pair breaking regimes.

B. Different pair breaking regimes

Although the AG theory was constructed specifically to treat the problem of superconductors with magnetic impurities, it has since been shown by de Gennes, Fulde, Maki and others that the theory can be adapted to treat other pair breaking situations

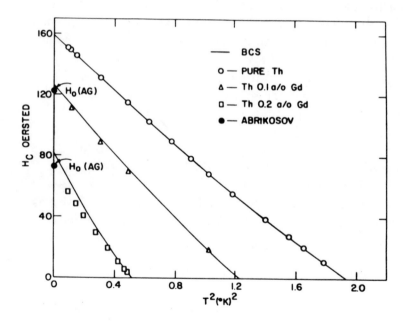

Fig. 17. Critical field behavior of $Th_{1-x}Gd_x$ compared
with prediction of AG theory (from Ref. 35).

which lead to second order superconducting normal
(s-n) phase transitions (e.g., see Refs. 23 and 36).
Examples of these are shown in Table 2. In each of
the cases cited (subject to the indicated constraints)
the s-n coexistence curve can be described by Eq.
(2) wherein the normalized pair breaking parameter
α/α_{cr} is appropriately redefined in each case. The
quantities H_{c2} (0), H_{c3} (0), $H_{c||}$ (0) and H_{c}'(0)
are the critical fields at $T = 0°K$ in the four cited
regimes. The origin pair breaking effect in regime
1 has been discussed at length above; in regime 2 it
is due to the fact that the two members of a Cooper
pair find themselves in different potentials. In
regimes 3-5 pair breaking can be attributed to high
current densities in the vortices, in the surface
sheath, or associated with the Meissner response
of a thin superconductor respectively. Simply stated,
when the kinetic energy of a pair (due to the high
current density) exceeds the binding energy of the
pair, the pair breaks leading to redistribution effects
in the Fermi distribution and a reduction in the condensation energy. In regime 6 the origin of the pair
breaking effect lies in the Zeeman effect on the
Cooper pair. The field tends to align the opposite
spin members of the pair in the same direction and
consequently the pair is broken when the Zeeman
energy μH exceeds the binding energy Δ.

The experimental verification of the AG theory
(in particular Eq. (2) and the density of states spectrum shown in Fig. 3) has been more perfectly
achieved in some of the other pair breaking regimes
listed in Table 2 than it has for regime 1. The reason
for this is that in regimes 1 or 2, a different sample
is required for the measurement of each point on

Table 2. Different pair breaking regimes

Regime	Normalized pair breaking parameter	Constraints
1. Superconductor with magnetic impurities	n/n_{cr}	----------
2. Thin superconductor in intimate contact with normal metal (proximity effect)	complicated	----------
3. The vortex state	$H/H_{c2}(0)$	$l \ll \xi_0$ (where l is the transport mean free path)
4. The surface sheath state	$H/H_{c3}(0)$	$l \ll \xi_0$
5. Thin superconductor in parallel magnetic field	$H^2/H_c^2(0)$	$l \ll \xi_0$ $d \ll \xi(T)$ (where d is thickness of superconductor)
6. Pauli paramagnetism	$H^2/H_c'^2(0)$	$l \ll \xi_0$ $l_{so} \ll \xi_0$ (where l_{so} is spin-orbit scattering mean free path)

the s-n coexistence curve, whereas in regimes 3-5, the curve can be obtained by using only one sample, in which case the pair breaking parameter α is varied by turning a knob (e.g., current supply to electromagnet) during the experiment. Beautiful results, for instance, have been obtained in regime 5 by Millstein and Tinkham [37] and independently by Levine.[38]

C. Multiple pair breaking regimes

In order to observe Pauli paramagnetism effects (regine 6) it is necessary that the applied magnetic field enter the sample. This can be accomplished only by subjecting the sample to a multiple pair breaking regime (e.g., regimes 3+6 or regimes 5+6). In the case of either a bulk type II superconductor or a thin film superconductor in a parallel magnetic field, the field enters the sample and may in fact be little depressed in the sample if in the first case $\kappa \gg 1$ and in the second case $d \ll \lambda$ (T). This brings us to the general problem of how to treat multiple pairbreaking situations. An interesting prediction of the "pair breaking school" (e.g. see Refs. 36, 39, and 40) is that in many multiple pair breaking regimes, Eq. (12), which we rewrite here for convenience

$$\ln\frac{T_c}{T_{co}} + \psi(\tfrac{1}{2} + 0.14\,\frac{T_c}{T_{co}}\,\frac{\alpha}{\alpha_{cr}}) - \psi(\tfrac{1}{2}) = 0, \tag{2}$$

still applies if one puts

$$\frac{\alpha}{\alpha_{cr}} = \sum_i \frac{\alpha}{\alpha_{cri}}, \tag{5}$$

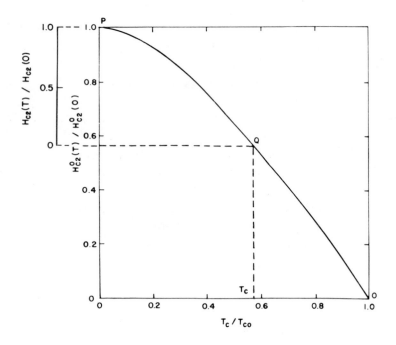

Fig. 18. Illustrative diagram showing significance of
multiple pair breaking theory [Eqs. (2) and (5)] for
double pair breaking regime (see text).

where α_{cri} is the value of the ith pair breaking parameter α_i required to suppress T_c to zero in the absence of the other ($j \neq i$) pair breaking perturbations. The validity of Eq. (5) rests on the same constraints required of the single pair breaking regimes in order that they be described by Eq. (2) (see Table 2).

The significance of the additivity expressed in Eq. (5) is illustrated in Fig. 18. Consider a double pair breaking regime, e.g., a type II superconductor with magnetic impurities in the presence of a magnetic field. The curve PQO is a plot of Eq. (2); it is also the normalized critical field curve, H_{c2}° (T)/H_{c2}° (0) vs. T/T_{co}, of the system in the pure limit (e.g. no magnetic impurities, $T_c = T_{co}$). Now if enough magnetic impurities are added to take us to point Q on the curve in zero field then the remaining portion of the curve PQ corresponds to the full normalized critical field curve, H_{c2} (T)/H_{c2} (0) vs. T/T_c of the system in the presence of magnetic impurities, T_c being the zero field transition temperature in the presence of the impurities.

In order to check the additivity relation expressed in Eqs. (2) and (5) Guertin et al. [41] studied two double pair breaking regimes. One study was the critical field behavior of the $(Th-5\%La)_{1-x}Er_x$ system. Thorium was chose as the host system because of the metallurgical compatibility of Th with the rare earths. Five percent La was added to the Th host to convert it to a type II superconductor thereby allowing access to pair breaking regime No. 3 (the vortex state). The addition of 5% La leads to an increase of κ from 0.5 to $\sim$ 4.0 as determined from critical field measurements. In this double pair breaking study, Eq. (5) takes the form

$$\frac{\alpha(T)}{\alpha_{cr}} = \frac{n}{n_{cr}} + \frac{H_{c2}(T)}{H_{c2}^{\circ}(0)} \qquad (6)$$

or alternatively,

$$\frac{\alpha(T)}{\alpha_{cr}} = \frac{\alpha(T_c)}{\alpha_{cr}} + \frac{H_{c2}(T)}{H_{c2}^{\circ}(0)} . \qquad (7)$$

It was found convenient, experimentally, to test the theory by measuring the dependence of $(dH_{c2}/dT)_{T_c}$ as a function of T_c (and therefore, x). The theoretical prediction for this dependence, derived from Eqs. (1) and (7) and shown in Fig. 20, is strikingly different from the BCS result, [4] $(dH_c/dT)_{T_c}$ = constant, which one would expect in a non-pair-breaking situation. The experimental results in Figs. 19 and 20 are seen to be in good agreement with the double pair breaking theory. A second test of the theory by Guertin et al.[41] consisted of measuring the critical field behavior of a thin superconducting film in contact with a normal magnetic metal (e.g. a combination of regimes 2 and 5 in Table 2). Again there was good agreement between theory and experiment.

D. Critical field studies of $InLa_{3-x}Gd_x$

The $InLa_{3-x}Gd_x$ system because of its high value of κ exhibits complicated but interesting behavior in the presence of a magnetic field. To properly treat the problem one must consider the simultaneous effect of spin scattering of the electrons from the magnetic impurities, momentum depairing of the electrons associated with the vortex state, and exchange enhanced Pauli paramagnetism effects. Critical field studies of this system were made by Crow, Guertin, and Parks, [42] the results of which are shown

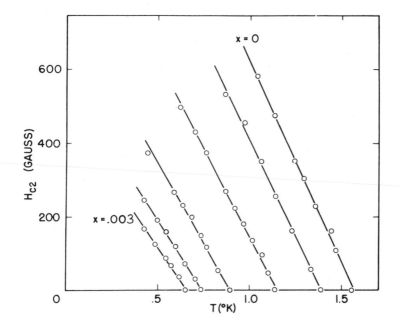

Fig. 19. Critical field curves for $(\text{Th-}5\%\text{La})_{1-x}\text{Er}_x$
alloys. (from Ref. 41).

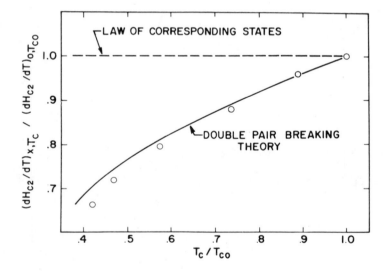

Fig. 20. Temperature derivative (evaluated at T_c) of the critical field curves of Fig. 19 vs. T_c/T_{co}. Results are compared with prediction of multiple pair breaking theory.

effects. Critical field studies of this system were
made by Crow, Guertin, and Parks,[42] the results
of which are shown in Figs. 21 and 22. The first
point to note is the enormous value of H_{c2} (0) of the
pure matrix which implies that $InLa_3$ is an intrinsic
type II superconductor with a very large value of
κ ($\gtrsim 20$). A second important feature is the rapid
depression of H_{c2} (for $T \approx 0^\bullet K$) with increasing
impurity concentrations. The ratio of H_{c2} (0) for
La_3In to that for a sample doped with 1.24 at % Gd
is greater than 10, whereas the ratio of the transition temperatures is about 2. Perhaps the most
striking feature is the fact that the curves are non-
monotonic for intermediate Gd concentrations.
Critical field curves which are periodic in temperature have been reported in connection with various
experiments concerning fluxoid quantization,[43, 44]
but I know of no other instance of reported critical
field curves which are non-monotonic with field.
An additional noteworthy feature of the results
in Fig. 22 is the leveling off of the curves for the
samples with 1.24 and 1.49 % Gd. It is possible to
understand semiquantitatively all of these observed
features by properly applying the multiple pair
breaking theory appropriate to regimes 1+3+6 (see
Table 2).

Before doing this I shall give a qualitative explanation of the cause of the non-monotonicity in the
curves in Fig. 22. This reflects the temperature
dependence of the exchange fields seen by the conduction electrons and was predicted by de Gennes
and Sarma.[45] We start with Eqs. (4) which give
the Pauli paramagnetism contribution to the free
energy of the superconducting and normal states.

R. D. PARKS

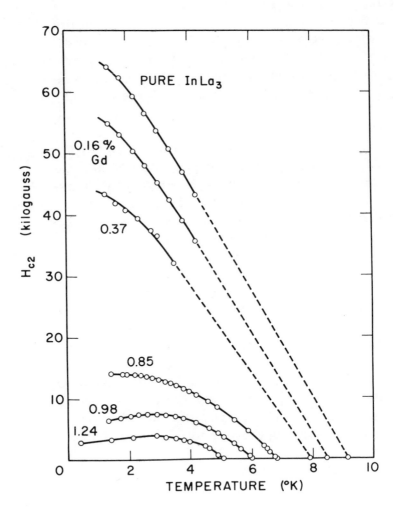

Fig. 21. Critical field curves of $InLa_{3-x}Gd_x$ alloys in the concentration range, 0-1.24 at % Gd (from Ref. 42).

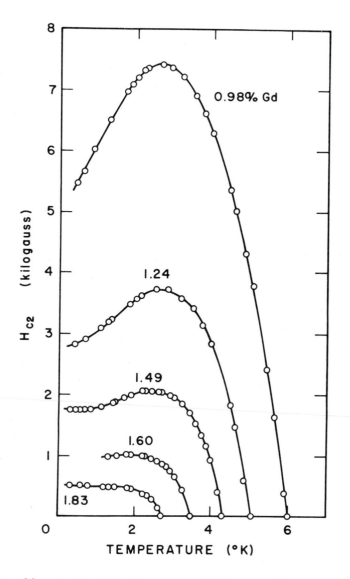

Fig. 22. Critical field curves of InLa$_{3-x}$Gd$_x$ alloys in the concentration range 0.98 - 1.83 at % Gd (from Ref. 42).

The difference in this contribution to the free energy between the normal and superconducting states is

$$\Delta FE_n^M - \Delta FE_s^M = -(\chi_p^n - \chi_p^s) \ H_{eff}^2.$$
(8)

Now, H_{eff} is a sum of the applied and internal exchange fields, given by

$$H_{eff} = AJ_{ex} \ \langle S_z \rangle + H_a,$$

where A is a quantity which depends upon various parameters of the host metal and is proportional to the spin impurity concentration, J_{ex} is proportional to the strength of the exchange interaction between the 4f electrons and the conduction electrons, $\langle S_z \rangle$ is the average z component of the impurity spin vector, and H_a the applied magnetic field. We consider two cases:

Case 1. ($T_m \ll T_c$, where T_m is the magnetic ordering temperature) In this case,

$$\langle S_z \rangle = SB \ (\mu H_a/kT),$$

where B is the Brillouin function. If in addition, $\mu H_a/kT \ll 1$, this simplifies to

$$\langle S_z \rangle \propto H_a/T$$

and we would have

$$\Delta FE_n^M - \Delta FE_s^M = -(\chi_p^n - \chi_p^s) \ (\frac{const}{T} + 1)^2 \ H_a^2$$
(11)

In short, the free energy difference between the normal
and superconducting states becomes more negative with
decreasing temperature which accounts qualitatively
for the decrease in the critical field with decreasing
temperature observed in Fig. 21. In a more complete
treatment of the problem one must include the fact
that there is another field dependent free energy contribution to the superconducting state, viz. that associated with the vortex state.

Case 2. ($T_m \gtrsim T_c$). In this case $\langle S_z \rangle$ is saturated
and we lose the temperature dependence found in
Case 1. For this case the critical field curves should
be monotonic. This suggests that for the samples
with 1.60 and 1.χ3 at % Gd the above criterion
($T_m \gtrsim T_c$) holds. The leveling off of the curves for
the samples with 1.24 and 1.49 at % Gd reflect presumably the onset of magnetic ordering at temperatures
below the peaks in the critical field curves.

To treat the problem more rigorously one must
go to the multiple pair breaking theory. For the
problem at hand, Eq. (5) takes the form

$$\frac{\propto}{\propto_{cr}} = \frac{n}{n_{cr}} + \frac{H_{c2}(T)}{H_{c2}^{\circ}(0)} + \frac{p}{p_{cr}} \tag{12}$$

where the Pauli susceptibility term P is given by

$$P = \tau_{so}(n\, J_{ex} \langle S_z \rangle)^2, \tag{13}$$

where τ_{so} is the spin-orbit scattering time and the
other terms have been previously defined. By judi-
ciously choosing the various parameters it is possible
to obtain semi-quantitative agreement between the

above theory and the results in Figs. 20 and 21.
(See discussion by Bennemann in these proceedings).
In order to ascertain that the s-n transition in
the presence of field was second order for the samples
studied above, magnetization measurements were
made on the samples with higher spin concentrations.
Cyrot[46] in an extension of the theory of de Gennes and
Sarma predicted that for higher Gd concentrations
the field induced transition at low temperatures
should become first order. No evidence for a first
order transition was found for the samples with
highest Gd concentration. The magnetization of the
sample with 1.83 at % Gd at T = 1.27°K as a function
of magnetic field is shown in Fig. 23. The arrow at
492 gauss corresponds to the s-n transition temperature determined by resistivity measurements.
If the transition were first order this should have
shown up as a kink in the magnetization curve in the
vicinity of the arrow. The magnetization curve is
unlike the curves characteristically obtained in
superconductivity studies since it is dominated by
the paramagnetic contribution. The large value of
kappa for the system is reflected in the large ratio
between H_{c2} (determined by the arrow) and H_{c1}
($\sim H_{peak}$).

E. Antiferromagnetic exchange

Let me conclude by mentioning some very interesting s-n phase diagrams which could result if
the s-f exchange interaction were antiferromagnetic,
but the RKKY coupling were to lead to a ferromagnetic alignment of the impurity spins. This would
imply that in the magnetically ordered state, the

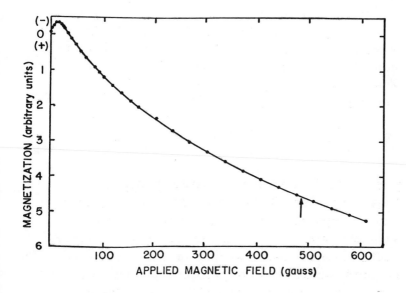

Fig. 23. Magnetization of $InLa_{3-x}Gd_x$ for a Gd concentration of 1.83 atomic percent vs. applied magnetic field ($T = 1.27°K$).

conduction electrons would be spin polarized in the direction opposite to the polarization of the impurity spin system. In the paramagnetic state, the application of a magnetic field H_a would cause a polarization of the impurity spins ($\langle S_z \rangle \neq 0$). This in turn would lead to an internal field H_{int} seen by the conduction electrons, which opposes the applied magnetic field. The effective field H_{eff} seen by the conduction electrons would be

$$H_{eff} = H_a + H_{int}$$

where $H_{int} = AJ_{ex} \langle S_z \rangle$ and A is a constant.

Now, suppose that a system such as the one described above is a type II superconductor immersed in an applied field. If the various relevant constraints in Table 2 are satisfied, one could describe the situation by Eq. (12) which for this case takes on the form,

$$\frac{\propto(T)}{\propto_{cr}} = \frac{n}{n_{cr}} + \frac{a\,H_a}{\kappa} + b\tau_{so}\,(H_a - H_{int})^2, \quad (14)$$

where a and b are uninteresting constants which depend upon sample paramaters. One can, in principle, suppress the vortex (second) term as much as is desired by increasing the value of κ. Suppose that κ is large enough so that the vortex (second) term is small compared to the Pauli paramagnetism (third) term. Consider first the case $T_m \ll T_c$, where T_m is the ferromagnetic Curie point. In this case

$$\langle S_z \rangle = SB\,(\mu H/kT)$$

and as H_a is increased H_{int} increases linearly with
H_a initially; then as the Brillouin function saturates,
$dH_{int}/dH_a \rightarrow 0$. If the quantity ($AJ_{ex}$) is sufficiently
large (which is easily realized experimentally),
there will be a range of H_a for which $|H_{int}|$ is larger
than $|H_a|$; but for sufficiently large $|H_a|$ one has
$|H_a| > |H_{int}|$ (because of the saturation of $\langle S_z \rangle$).
This results in a non-monotonic dependence on H_a of
the Pauli paramagnetism term in Eq. (14), which
in turn leads to the interesting multiphase diagram
shown in Fig. 24 (top). Points on the S'-N' and
S-N coexistence lines, where S, S' are superconducting phases and N, N' are normal phases, for a
given isotherm correspond to the same value of the
(non-monotonic) Pauli term in Eq. (14). At some
point in the S phase the applied and internal fields
are equal ($|H_a| = |H_{int}|$).

If $T_c < T_m$, this corresponds to $\langle S_z \rangle$ = const.,
H_{int} = const. and one obtains the lower phase diagram
in Fig. 24. In this case $T_c(H = 0)$ is determined not
just by the spin scattering term in Eq. (14), but also
by the Pauli term which has a non-zero value even in
zero applied field. The Pauli term decreases with
applied magnetic field initially and then increases
when H_a becomes larger than H_{int}.

The above effects, first suggested by Gruenberg
and Schwartz[47] have not been observed. We searched
for the effect in the $InLa_{3-x}Ce_x$ system,[48] but found
only conventional behavior. Cerium was chosen as
the spin impurity because Sugawara and Eguchi[49]
observed that $La_{1-x}Ce_x$ displays a resistivity minimum at low temperatures suggesting a Kondo effect
and therefore an antiferromagnetic s-f exchange
interaction. No resistivity minima have been

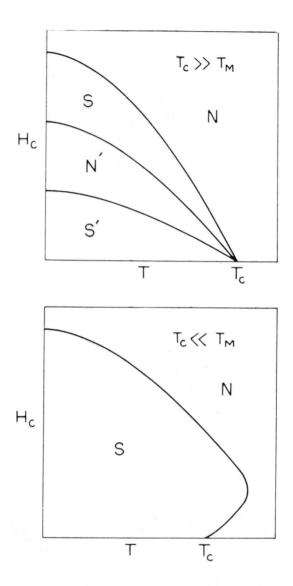

Fig. 24. Predicted phase diagrams for system with
antiferromagnetic s-f interaction.

observed in any of the other $La_{1-x}(RE)_x$ systems[49]
(RE = rare earth) or in any of the $Th_{1-x}(RE)_x$
systems including $Th_{1-x}Ce_x$.[50] We chose as the
host system $InLa_3$ because of its large value of
kappa which corresponds to a small contribution
of the vortex depairing term in Eq. (14). Our failure
to observe the expected behavior was due presumably
to (a) the s-f exchange interaction not being antiferromagnetic in $InLa_3$ or (b) our inability to ade-
quately suppress the vortex depairing term in Eq.
(14).

An alternative approach which is more promis-
ing is the one being pursued presently by Crow and
Strongin.[51] Their approach is to combine regimes
1, 5 and 6 (Table 2) instead of 1, 3 and 6, thereby
replacing the vortex term in Eq. (14) by the pair
breaking term cH^2/d^2 which describes momentum
depairing in a thin film in a parallel magnetic field
(c is an uninteresting constant and d the film thickness). By working with A1 films deposited on cryogenic substrates it is possible to make this term
ignorable small compared to the Pauli term.

ACKNOWLEDGMENTS

The author gratefully acknowledges support
from the Air Force Office of Scientific Research
under grant no. AFOSR-807-65 during the preparation of this article.

REFERENCES

1. E.g., see G. Gladstone, M. A. Jensen and J. R. Schrieffer, Superconductivity, edited by R. D. Parks (Marcel Dekker, Inc., New York, to be published).

2. E.g., see M. J. Zuckermann, Phys. Rev. 168, 390 (1968).

3. T. Kasuya, Progr. Theoret. Phys. (Kyoto) 16, 56 (1966).

4. J. Bardeen, L. N. Cooper and J. R. Schrieffer, Phys. Rev. 108, 1175 (1957).

5. B. T. Matthias, H. Suhl, and E. Corenzwit, Phys. Rev. Letters 1, 92 (1958).

6. P. W. Anderson, J. Phys. Chem. Solids 11, 26 (1959).

7. H. Suhl and B. T. Matthias, Phys. Rev. 114, 977 (1959).

8. J. Muller and M. Risi, Helv. Phys. Acta. 33, 459 (1960).

9. R. D. Parks, Bull. Am. Phys. Soc. 7, 322 (1962).

10. A. A. Abrikosov and L. P. Gor'kov, Zh. Eksperim. i Teor. Fiz. 42, 1088 (1962); English transl.: Soviet Phys.-JETP 15, 752 (1962).

11. S. Skalski, O. Betbeder-Matibet, and P. R. Weiss, Phys. Rev. 136, A1500 (1964).

12. M. A. Woolf and F. Reif, Phys. Rev. 137, A557 (1965).

13. D. K. Finnemore, D. L. Johnson, J. E. Ostenson, F. H. Spedding, and B. D. Beaudry, Phys. Rev. 137, A550 (1965).

14. R. A. Hein, R. L. Falge, Jr., B. T. Matthias, and E. Corenzwit, Phys. Rev. Letters 2, 500 (1959).

15. D. K. Finnemore, D. C. Hopkins, and P. E. Palmer, Phys. Rev. Letters 18, 891 (1965).

16. N. Phillips and B. T. Matthias, Phys. Rev. 121, 105 (1961).

17. J. E. Crow and R. D. Parks, Phys. Letters 21, 378 (1966).

18. K. H. Bennemann, Phys. Rev. Letters 17, 438 (1966).

19. R. A. Ferrell, Phys. Rev. Letters 3, 262 (1959).

20. P. W. Anderson, Phys. Rev. Letters 3, 325 (1959).

21. R. P. Guertin, J. E. Crow and R. D. Parks, Phys. Rev. Letters 16, 546 (1966).

22. D. K. Finnemore, L. J. Williams, F. H. Spedding and D. C. Hopkins, preprint.

23. E.g., see P. G. de Gennes, Superconductivity of Metals and Alloys (W. A. Benjamin, Inc., New York, 1966).

24. M. W. Klein, Phys. Rev. Letters 16, 90 (1966).

25. M. W. Klein, Phys. Rev. 141, 489 (1966).

26. M. W. Klein and R. Brout, Phys. Rev. 132, 2412 (1963).

27. M. Marshall, Phys. Rev. 118, 1520 (1960).

28. S. H. Liu, Phys. Rev. 157, 411 (1967).

29. R. P. Guertin and R. D. Parks, to be published.

30. L. P. Gor'kov and A. I. Rusinov, Zh. Eksperim. i Teor. Fix. 46, 1363 (1964); English trans.: Soviet Phys.-JETP 19, 922 (1964).

31. M. B. Maple, Phys. Letters 26A, 513 (1968).

32. P. W. Anderson and H. Suhl, Phys. Rev. 116, 898 (1959).

33. N. R. Werthamer, E. Halfand and P. C. Hohenberg, Phys. Rev. 147, 295 (1965).

34. P. Fulde and K. Maki, Phys. Rev. 139, A788 (1965).

35. W. R. Decker, D. T. Peterson, and D. K. Finnemore, Phys. Rev. Letters 18, 899 (1967).

36. K. Maki in Superconductivity, edited by R. D. Parks (Marcel Dekker, Inc., New York, to be published).

37. J. Millstein and M. Tinkham, Phys. Rev. 158, 325 (1967).

38. J. L. Levine, Phys. Rev. 155, 373 (1967).

39. P. Fulde and K. Maki, Phys. Rev. 141, 275 (1966).

40. P. Fulde and K. Maki, Phys. kondens. Materie 5, 380 (1966).

41. R. P. Guertin, W. E. Masker, T. W. Mihalisin, R. P. Groff and R. D. Parks, Phys. Rev. Letters 20, 387 (1968).

42. J. E. Crow, R. P. Guertin and R. D. Parks, Phys. Rev. Letters 19, 77 (1967).

43. R. D. Parks, W. A. Little, Phys. Rev. 133, A97 (1964).

44. R. D. Parks, J. M. Mochel and L. V. Surgent, Jr., Phys. Rev. Letters 13, 331a (1964).

45. P. G. de Gennes and G. Sarma, Solid State Commun. 4, 449 (1966).

46. M. Cyrot, private communication.

47. L. W. Gruenberg and B. B. Schwartz, Bull. Am. Phys. Soc. 13, 427 (1968).

48. J. E. Crow, R. P. Guertin, R. D. Parks, and K. Schürmann, unpublished, 1967.

49. T. Sugawara and H. Eguchi, J. Phys. Soc. (Japan) 21, 725 (1966).

50. D. T. Peterson, D. F. Page, R. B. Rump, and D. K. Finnemore, Phys. Rev. 153, 701 (1967)

51. J. Crow and M. Strongin, private communication.

TIME DEPENDENT
GINSBURG-LANDAU THEORIES

E. R. Pike

TIME DEPENDENT
GINSBURG-LANDAU THEORIES

E. R. Pike
Royal Radar Establishment
Malvern, Worcestershire, England

INTRODUCTION

We have heard many times in this school that
when situations are encountered in superconductivity
where the order parameter varies in space the phenomenological theory of Ginsburg and Landau[1], which
was put on a microscopic basis by Gorkov[2], is one
of the most useful techniques available. We have not
heard quite so much about the extensions of the theory,
which are valid down to lower temperatures, due to
Werthamer[3], Tewordt[4], and Zumino and Uhlenbrock[5]. These as yet, to my knowledge, have not
been widely applied. Extensions, on the other hand,
to cases where the order parameter varies not only in
space but also in time have formed the backbone of a
considerable amount of work which has been presented
here, in particular by Professor's Schmid and Maki.
Perhaps the most discussed of such problems has been
that of flux-flow resistivity in type II superconductors
where a resistance appears which is associated with
the motion of an Abrikosov vortex pattern at right angles
to the flow of a bulk transport current.

693

The result of such an experiment is shown in Fig.
1. Flux flow resistivity is plotted versus magnetic
field. This work was performed by Gough and Funnell
at Birmingham. Similar results have been obtained by
Vinen and Warren[6] and by Serin[7]. The sample was
high purity Niobium in the form of a long cylinder.
This was placed in an exial magnetic field and subjected
to a small extra applied field by passing a square wave
of current through an auxiliary coil wrapped around it.
A second "pick-up" coil was used to observe the change
of magnetic flux and by a standard analysis the flux-
flow resistivity was determined. The reason why I
show this particular work is that the results deviate so
much from the existing predictions, and it highlights the
fact that in the clean limit there is still much to be
understood. Present theories do not account for the
abrupt change in slope at H_{c2}. Similar discrepancies
exist at the present time with regard to measurements
of ultrasonic attenuation and thermal conductivity in
this limit.

THE THEORETICAL PROBLEM

I am afraid that I am not going to be able to tell
you what the answers are to these difficult time-
dependent problems, but I shall try to review a little
the attempts to obtain time-dependent generalisations
of the Ginsburg-Landau theory and to see which way we
might go to improve the present situation. The problem
is basically one in non-equilibrium statistical mechanics. The total system is initially described by the
co-ordinates and Hamiltonian of an interacting set of
electrons and phonons, in an external time-dependent

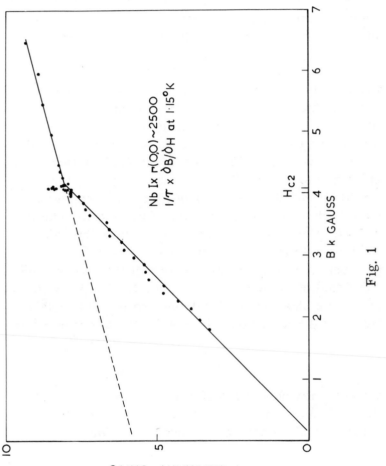

Nb Ix r(OO)~2500
$1/\tau \times \delta B/\delta H$ at 1.15°K

H_{c2}

B k GAUSS

ARBITRARY UNITS

Fig. 1

electromagnetic field. The first step in such problems
is to try to divide the total system up into a set of sub-
systems which only interact weakly with each other or
which interact in a well-defined simple way. These
interactions can then be dealt with, by for example,
perturbation theory, and the equations governing the
part of the system of particular interest extracted from
those of the complete system. In the superconductivity
problem the total system can be considered to be made
up of four interacting parts; a field of quasi particles,
a field of pairs, a phonon heat bath, and the external
fields. The interacting systems of quasi particles and
pairs are specified by the B.C.S. theory or later modi-
fications, and the reservoir of phonons provides, in the
equilibrium case, a temperature for the quasi particle
and pair fields. We shall discuss shortly the role of
the heat bath in the non-equilibrium case.

Let us call the density matrix of the total system
ρ and that of the parts σ, q, p and r for the pairs, quasi-
particles, phonons and electromagnetic fields respectively. A first approximation would be to assume that

$$\rho = \sigma \; qpr$$

We know however, for instance from the work of Lax[8],
that such a factorization does not lead to irreversible
behavior and we need to go further to a form

$$\rho = \sigma \; qpr + \Delta\rho$$

where $\Delta\rho$ may be treated as a first-order correction.
If we do this in a slowly varying approximation and
trace over the variables of the quasi-particles, heat
reservoir and e.m. field we shall end up with an equation

for the behaviour of the pair field. This will have the form of a wave equation if the interactions between pairs and between particles and also the interactions with the phonon field are neglected and becomes a damped wave equation when these are added. The damping is smaller at low temperatures and for high-frequency disturbances, the action of the heat bath being to even out local variations in the order parameter from its thermal equilibrium value. In sound propagation in solids for instance there are two limiting cases, isothermal and adiabatic, where the local temperature follows or does not follow the distortion wave.

We must now ask how, technically, do we cope with these various situations. The method that we have been shown by Professor Schmid and Maki at this meeting, which has also been used by Tsuneto and Abrahams[9], and Abrahams and Woo[10] is that of the imaginary-time thermal Green's functions of Matsubara. This is a linear response theory about zero order parameter in which the quasi-particle and pair fields are set in thermal equilibrium at $t = -\infty$ and the external fields are then applied adiabatically until time t. The heat bath may be considered to be removed at the time the fields are applied since corrections for further interaction would be of higher order. Any thermal damping, therefore, can only arise if electron electron or pair-pair thermalising interactions are included. This conclusion seems to be at variance with the results of Schmid[11], Abrahams and Woo[10], Abrahams and Tsuneto[9] and Caroli and Maki[12] who found various damping terms using this technique. This is a delicate point but Schmid, for instance, has explained in his lectures that the technique does not work below T_c since a branch point appears which prevents the analytic continuation being performed. He has circumvented this by introducing the extra interactions which are required in his specification of the unperturbed Green's function. The effect of the possible vanishing of the gap parameter on these considerations is not clear.

A different technique which has been used by Dr. Jakeman and myself is an extended form of the analytic thermal Greens function[14]. In our time-dependent extension of this technique the heat bath is assumed to act very rapidly compared with other processes taking place so that we have the situation which applies when considering isothermal sound waves. The time variable appears only locally in this theory, which we feel must always apply when the time dependence is sufficiently slow. No dissipation occurs again since the damping is infinitely rapid. Our results are identical to those of the phenomenological theory of Kulik[13]. A full theory is not yet available in which the heat bath has an intermediate effect.

SMALL DAMPING CASE

The case where heavy damping occurs has been discussed at length by Schmid and Maki and I shall consider here the opposite case of small damping. The domains of applicability of these limiting cases are not clear at the present time but we note that Professor Stephen has found a situation where the damping can be neglected in his treatment of tunnelling junctions.

The basic problem which we solve is that of finding the properties of a system described by the Hamiltonian (for each spin)

$$H(t)\!\int = \Psi^*(r,t)\Big\{\frac{1}{2m}\Big[\,i\nabla_r + \frac{eA}{c}(r,t)\Big]^2$$

$$+ e\phi(r,t) - \mu^0\Big\}\ \Psi(r,t)\,dr$$

$$-\frac{J}{2}\int \Psi^*(r,t)\ \Psi^*(r,t)\ \Psi(r,t)\ \Psi(r,t)\,dr$$

$$= \int \Psi^*(r,t)\ (T(r,t) - \mu_0)\ \Psi(r,t)\,dr$$

$$-\frac{J}{2}\int \Psi^*(r,t)\ \Psi^*(r,t)\ \Psi(r,t)\ \Psi(r,t)\,dr$$

in the approximation that a semiclassical expansion
is made up to and including second-order terms in
the gradients of the potentials and that the wave
function has B.C.S. form.

The single-particle term is straightforward save
that we have referred all single-particle energies to
a reference level μ^0 in order to simplify the further
algebra a little. This reference level is defined by
the equation for the total number of particles

$$N = \int \rho\,(r,\mu^0)\,dr$$

and its use makes some single-particle energy and
momentum integrals vanish on parity grounds. The
interaction term must be gauge invariant and its
transformation properties restrict its form. We require an approximation to the attractive interaction

near the Fermi surface which gives rise to superconductivity, the B.C.S. approximation is velocity dependent and hence not gauge invariantè we take the local
interaction used by Gorkov which we expect to be
resonable when the effects which we are studying vary
little over the coherence distance.

The method used for the solution of this problem
is, as mentioned above, an extended theory of analytic
energy-dependent Green's functions. The extensions
were in three directions: the first was to include a
"centre of gravity" time variable as well as the "difference" time variable of the equilibrium theory, the
second was to transform the whole theory into phase
space using the Wigner distribution functions, and the
third was to convert the Green's functions to gauge-
invariant form to retain physical sense in each order
of approximation.

I am afraid that in a short lecture I cannot go into
too many details of the theory and I shall summarize
the way it works in a set of instructions. I hope that
those of you who are familiar with the techniques of
ordinary Green's functions will find these to a natural
extension and those who have not used Green's function
methods will have to take the results on trust until they
can work them out for themselves.

The basic object which one requires to calculate is
the correlation function in the co-ordinate representation

$$F\left(\underset{\sim\sim}{rr'}, tt'\right) = \langle \Psi^*\left(\underset{\sim}{r},t\right) \Psi\left(\underset{\sim}{r},t'\right)\rangle$$

where the angle brackets denote a grand-canonical average.

All the single-particle properties of the system
may be derived from the diagonal elements of this

correlation function and other properties follow from
the complete function. In particular the charge density
is

$$\rho(\underset{\sim}{r},t) = F(\underset{\sim}{r},\underset{\sim}{r},t,t)$$

and the current density

$$j(r,t) \propto \lim_{\underset{\sim}{r}\to\underset{\sim}{r}'} (\nabla_{\underset{\sim}{r}} - \nabla_{\underset{\sim}{r}'}) F(\underset{\sim}{r}\underset{\sim}{r}',tt)$$

The correlation function satisfies a rather complicated
differential equation, however, and the Green's function
method, basically, consists of applying a generalised
Laplace transform to this equation to render it alge-
braic. This usually results in a simpler problem and
the solution may be inverted to regain the correlation
functions and hence the physical properties of the
system. In the usual technique the temperature is introduced in the transforming process in such a way
that a fermi factor (or bose factor) is automatically
associated with the elementary excitations arising in
the solution. The transformed correlation function is
called the Green's function and is defined by

$$G(\underset{\sim}{r},\underset{\sim}{r}', T,E) = \frac{1}{2\pi} \int_{-\infty}^{+\infty} \frac{1 + e^{-\beta\omega}}{E - \omega} \int_{-\infty}^{+\infty} F(\underset{\sim}{r},\underset{\sim}{r}',T,\tau)$$

$$e^{i\omega\tau}d\omega d\tau = G(\Psi(\underset{\sim}{r}); \Psi^*(\underset{\sim}{r}'))$$

We have retained here the "centre of gravity" time
variable and we now introduce the other two extensions.

The phase-space transformation or "mixed representation" is made by using the formula for any operator

$$0(\underset{\sim}{r};\underset{\sim}{p}) = \int 0(\underset{\sim}{r} - \underset{\sim}{r}'/2, \underset{\sim}{r} + \underset{\sim}{r}'/2) \, e^{i\underset{\sim}{p}.\underset{\sim}{r}'} \, d\underset{\sim}{r}$$

It is well known that this transformation when performed on a product leads to

$$\int ABe^{ipr'} \, dr' = \lim_{\substack{r' \to r \\ p' \to p}} \exp\frac{i}{2}\left\{ \left(\frac{\partial}{\partial r}\frac{\partial}{\partial p'} - \frac{\partial}{\partial p}\frac{\partial}{\partial r'} \right) \right.$$

$$\left. A(r,p)\,B(r'p') \right\}$$

The phase-space transform may be combined with the fourier transform in the definition of the Green's function and the two may be expressed in terms of 4-dimensional variables $\underset{\sim}{r},T$ and $\underset{\sim}{p},E$ which we call r and p. We have then

$$G(r,p) = \frac{1}{2\pi} \int_{-\infty}^{+\infty} \frac{1-e^{-\beta\omega}}{E-\omega} \int_{-\infty}^{+\infty} F(\underset{\sim}{r}\underset{\sim}{r}'T\tau) \, e^{ip^T} \, d\omega \, d\tau$$

$$d(\underset{\sim}{r}-\underset{\sim}{r}')$$

The final extension is to define gauge-invariant functions following Zumino and Uhlenbrock[5] by the relation

$$\underset{\sim}{G}(r\,r') = G(r\,r') \exp i \int_{r}^{r'} (\frac{e}{c} \underset{\sim}{A}(s), - e\phi(s)) d\underset{\sim}{s}$$

which, using the notation

$$A = \left(\frac{eA}{c}, -e\phi\right)$$

and working to second order in the gradients gives rise to the relation

$$G(r;p) = \left\{1 + A.\nabla p + \frac{1}{2}(A.\nabla p)^2\right\} G(r;p)$$

The inverse transform in the equilibrium theory is

$$F(\mathbf{rr'},\tau) = 2\pi \Sigma \text{ residues of } \frac{G(\mathbf{rr'}E)e^{-iE\tau}}{e^{\beta E} + 1}$$

A shorthand notation for this process is

$$F(\mathbf{r,r'},\tau) = \int_E G(\mathbf{rr'}E) \, dE.$$

We shall only require diagonal terms in the inversion and these are found from the phase-space functions by

$$F(\mathbf{r},\tau) = \int\int_E G(\mathbf{r},pE) \, dp \, dE$$

$$\rho(r) = \int\int_E G(r;p) \, dp \, dE$$

$$j(r) = \frac{e}{m} \int\int_E p \, G(r;p) \, dp \, dE$$

The equation for the Green's function in the equilibrium theory is found by using the Hamiltonian of the problem in the basic relation

$$EG(\Psi(r); \Psi^*(r')) = \frac{1}{2\pi} + G([\Psi(r),H]; \Psi^*(r'))$$

The assumption of a B.C.S. type wave function or a "Gorkov decoupling" allows one to deduce two coupled equations

$$(E-T)\ G - \Delta\Gamma^* = \frac{1}{2\pi}$$

$$(E+T)T^* - \Delta^*G = 0$$

where

$$\Delta(r) = J \int_E \Gamma\ dE$$

and

$$\Gamma = G(\Psi(r); \Psi(r))$$

The extension of these Gorkov equations for $G(r,p)$ is

$$\frac{i}{2}\ \frac{dG(r,p)}{dT} - EG(r,p) - \lim_{\substack{r' \to r \\ t' \to t}} \exp\left\{\frac{i}{2}\ (\nabla_r \nabla_p - \nabla_p \nabla_r)\right.$$

$$(TG + \Delta\Gamma^*)\left.\right\}\frac{1}{2\pi}$$

and

$$\frac{i}{2}\ \frac{d\Gamma^*}{dT} - E\Gamma^* + \lim_{\substack{r' \to r \\ t' \to t}} \exp\left\{\frac{i}{2}\ (\nabla_r \nabla_p - \nabla_p \nabla_r)\right.$$

$$(T^*\Gamma^* - \Delta^*G)\left.\right\} = 0$$

The gauge covariant form of Γ is

$$\Gamma(r,p) = \left\{ 1 + \frac{i}{4} (\nabla_p \quad \nabla_r)(A \cdot \nabla_p) \right\} \Gamma(r,p)$$

Using these extended Gorkov equations we can calculate the values of G and Γ in various semiclassical orders. We have

$$G = G_0 + G_1 + G_2 \qquad \Gamma = \Gamma_0 + \Gamma_1 + \Gamma_2$$

$$T = T_0 + T_1 + T_2$$

$$T_0 = \frac{p^2}{2m} - \mu^0$$

$$T_1 = (\frac{e}{mc} A.p + e\phi)$$

$$T_2 = \frac{e^2}{2mc^2} A^2$$

Quite a lengthy calculation is involved in finding G and Γ correctly to the second-order terms and we hope that we have not made any mistakes. Gauge invariance of the results is a good check. The answers for the zeroth and first-order terms are as follow

$$G_0 = \frac{1}{E - T_0 - \dfrac{|\Delta|^2}{E + T_0}}$$

$$G_1 = G_0^2 \left[2|\Delta|^2 A - \frac{i}{2} (\Delta \nabla_r \Delta - \Delta^* \nabla_r \Delta) \right] \nabla_p \frac{1}{T_0 - E}$$

$$\Gamma_0 = -\frac{\Delta}{E^2 - T_0^2 - |\Delta|^2}$$

$$\Gamma_1 = i\left(\frac{\Gamma_0}{\Delta}\right)^2 \left[E \frac{p}{m} \cdot (\nabla_r - 2\frac{ie}{c} A) \Delta - T_0 (\frac{\partial}{\partial t} \right.$$

$$\left. + 2ie\phi) \Delta \right]$$

The expressions for G_2 and Γ_2 are very long and will not be written down.

The final equations for the charge density, current and energy gap are as follows in the limit of small Δ.

$$e\rho = e\rho_0 - \frac{3emN}{p_f^2} \frac{7}{8} \frac{\zeta(3)}{(\pi T)^2} \left[2|\Delta|^2 e\phi \right.$$

$$+ \frac{i}{2} (\Delta \frac{\partial \Delta^*}{\partial t} - \Delta^* \frac{\partial \Delta}{\partial t}) + \frac{1}{2m} (\nabla_r - \frac{2ieA}{c}) \Delta$$

$$\left. (\nabla_r + \frac{2ieA}{c}) \Delta^* \right]$$

$$j = - \frac{eN}{m} \frac{7}{8} \frac{\zeta(3)}{(\pi T)^2} \left[2|\Delta|^2 \frac{e}{c} A - \frac{i}{2} (\Delta\nabla\Delta^* - \Delta^*\nabla\Delta) \right]$$

$$0 = \left[\log \frac{T_c}{T} - \frac{7}{8} \frac{\zeta(3)}{(\pi T)^2} |\Delta| + \frac{v_f^2}{6} \frac{7}{8} \frac{\zeta(3)}{(\pi T)^2} (\nabla_r \right.$$

$$\left. + \frac{2ieA}{c})^2 - \frac{1}{2} \frac{7}{8} \frac{\zeta(3)}{(\pi T)^2} (\frac{\partial}{\partial t} - 2ie\phi)^2 \right] \Delta^* = 0.$$

More complete results are given in reference (15).

The last of these three equations can be written in terms of a "pair-wave function"

$$\Psi = \Delta \left[7N \zeta(3) \right]^{1/2} / 4\pi T$$

as follows

$$\left\{ \frac{1}{2m} \left[\left(\nabla + \frac{2ieA}{c} \right)^2 - \frac{3}{v_f^2} \left(\frac{\partial}{\partial t} - 2ie\, \phi \right)^2 \right] \right.$$

$$\left. + \frac{24(\pi T)^2}{7\ \zeta(3)\ mv_f^2} \left[\log \frac{T_c}{T} - \frac{2}{N} |\Psi|^2 \right] \right\} \Psi^* = 0$$

This is a non-linear equation for the pair field which generalises, in a gauge-invariant way, the time-independent Ginsburg-Landau equation. The imaginary part of this equation is just the condition for charge conservation

$$\frac{\partial \rho}{\partial t} = \nabla . J$$

when the equations for ρ and J are substituted.

The non-linear inhomogeneous nature of the pair-field equation (gap equation) gives it certain two-fluid properties. We consider firstly solutions for which the phase only varies in time, corresponding say to the plane-wave solutions of a free single particle. The equation then becomes a Klein-Gordon equation[16] where $(mc)^2$ is given by

$$\frac{6}{v_f^2} \, (\, |\Delta|^2 - |\Delta_0|^2).$$

The charge equation for a Klein-Gordon field allows
changes of sign for the charge density, which is not
physical for a single-particle field. Here, however,
a variation of Ψ can result in either a positive or negative local variation in charge and no difficulty arises.
The simplest system to visualise which obeys the
Klein-Gordon equation is an elastic string embedded
in an elastic medium. Space-like decay of waves
occurs at low frequencies while propagation occurs
at high frequencies where the influence of the second
medium is negligible. In our case $(mc)^2$ can go negative which then results in time-like decay of waves
of long wavelength and does not have an analogy in the
two elastic media. In the absence of fields the dispersion relation for phase waves can easily be shown
to be

$$v_{phase} = \frac{\omega^2}{k^2} = \frac{v_f^2}{3} + \frac{2}{\hbar^2 k^2} \, (\, |\Delta|^2 - |\Delta_0|^2)$$

The phase velocity of these waves is thus a function of
amplitude.

A second type of solution which can be found is one
in which only the amplitude of the wave function varies.
In the absence of fields and space gradients the gap
equation can be solved analytically in terms of
Weierstrass' elliptic functions[17] and the solution in
general then oscillates indefinitely about the thermal
equilibrium value.

Care must be taken when linearizing the gap equation below T_c since relaxation to the bifurcated trivial solution $\Delta = 0$ of higher free energy is also obtained and must be rejected.

THIRD GINSBURG-LANDAU EQUATIONS

The system of three equations for charge density, current density and gap obtained above are self consistent, gauge invariant and conserve charge. The charge density must be allowed to vary in space and time to obtain this self consistancy but in the time-independent case the spatial variation is usually small and ignored. The equation becomes more important in the time-dependent case and a large number of attempts to guess or calculate its correct form have appeared in the literature of superconductivity by the use of either two-fluid phenomenology or microscopic theory. It should, amongst other properties, correctly describe the Josephson effect. To conclude I give a number of these previous results with brief comments. Desirable features of a derivation are that non-linear terms are included, spatial variation of the charge density is allowed (compressibility) and that microscopic theory is used. With each equation these features are discussed.

London[18]

$$\frac{m \partial v_s}{\partial t} = eE - \frac{1}{2} \nabla \left(mv_s^2 \right)$$

v_s is the superfluid velocity $(=\frac{e}{mc} (\mathbf{A} - \nabla W)$, where $2 eW/c$ is the phase of the pair wave function). This equation contains a non-linear term and is derived for an incompressible pure superfluid. London suggested the addition of an "osmotic pressure gradient" term for any normal fluid present in order to neutralise any space charges set up by the superfluid since the two-fluid theory would require any normal component to move in the presence of an electric field.

Bardeen and Stephen[19]

$$\frac{m\partial v_s}{\partial t} = e\mathbf{E} - \frac{1}{2} \nabla(mv_s^2) - \nabla\mu_0$$

This has non-linear and compressibility terms but is phenomenological. μ_0 is stated to be "the chemical photential per unit mass in the absence of currents or field".

Stephen[20]

$$\frac{m\partial v_s}{\partial t} = e\mathbf{E} - \frac{1}{2} \nabla(mv_s^2) - \nabla(e\phi - \frac{1}{2} mv_s^2 + \frac{e}{c} \frac{\partial W}{\partial t})$$

This has non-linear and compressibility terms and is based on a Boltzmann equation for the electrons which can be used to derive a two-fluid model by making certain assumptions about its solutions. The last term is called the gradient of the chemical potential but is not calculated further and the equation is only an identity if v_s is defined as above.

Anderson, Werthamer and Luttinger[21]

$$\frac{m\partial v_s}{\partial t} = e\mathbf{E} - \frac{e}{c} \nabla \left(\frac{\partial W}{\partial t}\right)$$

This has neither non-linear nor compressibility terms and is based on simple general phenomenological arguments. From the identity of Stephen above it can also be seen to be wrong.

Rickayzen[22]

$$\frac{m\partial v_s}{\partial t} = e\mathbf{E} - \frac{\rho_s}{2\rho} \nabla (mv^2)$$

This equation is non-linear and takes account of compressibility; it is phenomenological, however, and is said to be valid in the dirty limit.

Vinen[23]

$$\frac{m\partial v_s}{\partial t} = e\mathbf{E} - \frac{1}{2} \nabla (mv_s^2) - \nabla \left[\frac{p}{\rho} - \frac{\rho_n}{2\rho} (v_s - v_n)^2\right]$$

Accounts for compressibility and is non-linear. The "chemical potential" now contains dynamic information, is it should, but the derivation is entirely from two-luid phenomenology and is due to Landau save that Vinen asserts that μ does not contain the electrostatic potential. Meservey[24] obtains the same result.

Nozieres[25]

$$\frac{m\partial v_s}{\partial t} = eE - \frac{1}{2} \nabla (mv_s^2) - \nabla\mu$$

This formula is derived by invariance arguments in the pure limit and Nozieres suggests that $\nabla\mu$ should always be negligible.

Van Vijfeijken and Staas[25]

$$\frac{m\partial v_s}{\partial t} = eE - \frac{1}{2} \nabla (mv_s^2) + \frac{1}{\rho} \nabla p$$

This is a non-linear theory and the effects of compressibility were conjectured by coupling in an equation for the normal electrons. In the steady-state the last term on the right-hand side now dominates the first

$$\frac{1}{\rho} \nabla p = \frac{\rho_n}{\rho_s} eE$$

The same result is obtained by Vinen and by Meservey in the steady state ($v_n = 0$) by neglecting $1/\rho \nabla p$ but including the term

$$\frac{\rho_n}{\rho} \nabla v_s^2$$

Stephen and Suhl[27]

$$\frac{m \partial v_s}{\partial t} = \frac{\rho_0}{\rho_s} eE + \lambda_D^2 \frac{\rho_0}{\rho s} \nabla(\nabla.E)$$

This is a linear equation but contains the effects of compressibility and comes from the microscopic theory for the pure limit. Some interpretation has been required to arrive at an equation for comparison. λ_D is the Debye screening length defined by

$$\left(mv_f^2 / 12 \ \pi e\rho_0\right)^{1/2}$$

Further restrictions in Stephen and Suhl's derivation are that the frequency ω and wave number q of the disturbance obey the relations

$$\omega < |\Delta|$$

$$q < 1/\zeta_0$$

$$\omega \ll qv_f$$

Jakeman and Pike[28]

$$\frac{m \partial v_s}{\partial t} = \frac{\rho_0}{\rho_s} eE - \nabla(mv_s^2) + \lambda_D^2 \frac{\rho_0}{\rho_s} \nabla(\nabla.E)$$

This equation results from the theory outlined in this paper with the addition of a term

$$+ \frac{3e}{mv_f^2} \rho_n \int^r E.dS$$

to the charge equation to account for the normal-electron response. This ad hoc addition is necessary to overcome a difficulty of the theory which results from the fact that the classical response is non-local in the fields and "blows up" in the limit of zero spatial and temporal frequencies. When calculated in the potentials the classical response is local but a gauge-invariant formalism (which must be physical) is then not possible. The result is that these terms do not appear in the phase space slowly varying approximation. To improve the theory one might consider working in a fixed gauge, which presents some further difficulties, or try to calculate not the Green's function but its total derivative, which is local in the fields. The local theory will then provide a particular integral and the classical response will appear as the added complementary function.

The form of the equation presented above is most easily derived by using Stephen's identity and substituting the value of $\nabla \partial W / \partial t$ obtained from the charge equation; Poisson's equation is also used.

CONCLUSIONS

I have surveyed many attempts to obtain a time-dependent extension of the Ginsburg-Landau theory and have shown that at present there is no good universal theory. The experimental results for the flux-flow resistivity and other quantities in the clean limit remains unexplained; existing theories predict the wrong dependence on magnetic field. (The flux-flow resistivity for the small damping theory of Dr. Jakeman and myself has been calculated in the paper of Kulik[13]). The problem, as I hope I have conveyed, is a very complicated one and I feel myself that its proper solution might hinge on the development of more powerful ways of dealing with the interactions with the heat bath and within the field systems than have been used up to the present time. We can look perhaps for guidance at the recent solutions[29] of the time-dependent laser problem in which the behavior of the electromagnetic field bears a strong resemblance to that of the pair field in superconductivity.

REFERENCES

1. V. L. Ginzburg and L. D. Landau, J. Exptl. Theoret. Phys. (U.S.S.R.) **20**, 1064 (1950)

2. L. P. Gorkov, Soviet Physics JETP, **36**, 1364 (1950)

3. N. R. Werthamer, Phys. Rev. **132**, 663 (1963)

4. L. Tewordt, Phys. Rev. **132**, 595 (1963)

5. B. Zumino and D. A. Uhlenbrock, Nuova Cimento **33**, 1446 (1964)

6. W. F. Vinen and A. C. Warren, Proc. Phys. Soc., **91**, 399 (1967)

7. A. T. Fiory and B. Serin, Phys. Rev. Letts., **21**, 359-361, (1968).

8. M. Lax, Phys. Rev. **157**, 213 (1967). This paper contains references to the author's previous work.

9. E. Abrahams and T. Tsuneto, Phys. Rev., **152**, 416 (1966)

10. J. W. F. Woo and E. Abrahams, Phys. Rev., **169**, 407 (1968)

11. A. Schmid, Physik Kondensierten Materie, 5, 302 (1966)

12. C. Caroli and K. Maki, Phys. Rev., **164**, 591 (1967)

13. I. O. Kulik, Soviet Physics JETP, **23**, 1077 (1966)

14. D. N. Zubarev, Soviet Physics Uspekhi, **3**, 320 (1960)

15. E. R. Pike, Quantum Fluids, Ed. D. F. Brewer, North-Holland (1966)

16. P. M. Morse and H. Feshbach, Methods of Theoretical Physics, McGraw-Hill (1953)

17. A. Erdelyi, W. Magnus, F. Oberhettinger, F. G. Tricomi, Higher Trancendental Functions, Vol. 2, McGraw-Hill (1953).

18. F. London, Superfluids, Vol. 1, John Wiley (1950)

19. J. Bardeen and M. J. Stephen, Phys. Rev., **140**, A119 (1965)

20. M. J. Stephen, Phys. Rev., **139**, A197 (1965)

21. P. W. Anderson, N. R. Werthamer and J. M. Luttinger, Phys. Rev., **138**, A1157 (1965)

22. G. Rickayzen, Proc. Phys. Soc., **89**, 129-34, (1966)

23. W. F. Vinen, Quantum Fluids, Ed. D. F. Brewer, North Holland, pp. 74-108, 1966.

24. R. Meservey, Phys. Fluids **8**, 1209 (1965)

25. P. Nozieres, Quantum Fluids, Ed. D. F. Brewer, North Holland, pp. 1-22, 1966.

26. A. G. van Vijfeijken and F. A. Staas, Phys. Letts., **12**, 175 (1964)

27. M. J. Stephen and H. Suhl, Phys. Rev. Letts., **13**, 797 (1964)

28. E. Jakeman and E. R. Pike, Phys. Letts., **20**, 593 (1966)

29. For a review see H. Haken and W. Weidlich, Proceedings of the International School of Physics, "Enrico Fermi" (1967).

TUNNELING AND SUPERCONDUCTIVITY

J. M. Rowell

TUNNELING AND SUPERCONDUCTIVITY

J. M. Rowell
Bell Telephone Laboratories, Inc.
Murray Hill, New Jersey

After listening to the lectures given earlier this week, you will realize that most of the material I could include in this talk has already been discussed. The experiment is now a course exercise in Dr. Tinkham's laboratory, the physics of the electron phonon-interaction has been presented by Dr. Jensen, the theory of superconductivity and the use of the Eliashberg equation to calculate the gap and tunneling density of states has been discussed by Dr. Carbotte. Therefore, as nobody else has covered this topic, in this first lecture I will discuss very simply the notion of tunneling and show you how it has been used to measure a few simple properties of superconductors. I am not making any attempt to review the field and have selected only those experiments which illustrate a particular point. The level of the talk will be elementary compared to many of those earlier, some of you may find it a chance to catch your breath.

The first question one can ask is, as tunnel junctions are by reputation a difficult experimental system to manufacture, what can we do with tunneling that we cannot do with pieces of bulk metal, wires or films for example. Imagine a wire of normal metal and apply a

potential to it. A current flows which means electrons
are accelerated along each mean free path but lose
that energy by collisions with the lattice or other electrons. As long as the wire has a uniform density of
scattering centers the applied potential is distributed
along the length of the wire. This means that electrons
which enter the metal at the Fermi level also exit from
the metal very close to the Fermi level. Of course if
our metal were a semiconductor and we applied moder-
ately large voltages, the electron distribution would get
"hotter" than the lattice and electrons could have energies well above the Fermi level.

Now insert into the middle of the wire a thick insulating layer and apply the same voltage. All the potential appears across the insulator and no current flows.
If we could produce such a layer and slowly reduce its
thickness we would find that when the separation is $\sim 30 \overset{\circ}{\mathrm{A}}$
a measurable current would begin to flow. This arises
from the small chance an electron in metal (1) has of
appearing in metal (2) by tunneling through the insulating
barrier region. As the transmission probability has an
order of magnitude $\exp(-d\varphi^{1/2}) \sim \exp(-20)$ (d = barrier
thickness in $\overset{\circ}{\mathrm{A}}$, say 20$\overset{\circ}{\mathrm{A}}$; φ = barrier height in volts, say
1v) we can still let all the voltage drop across the bar-
rier. You can see immediately that the advantage of the
tunnel junction over the bulk metal is that we inject "hot"
electrons into metal (2), in fact we inject a band of electrons with energy ϵ [relative to the Fermi level in (2)]
of $0 \leq \epsilon \leq eV$. During this talk I would like to mention
a few assumptions which have been implicit in all treat-
ments of thin film tunneling and mention why, during the
past two years, we have realized that they are wrong.
The first of these is obvious from Fig. 3, that is we assume that no electrons lose any energy during the tun-

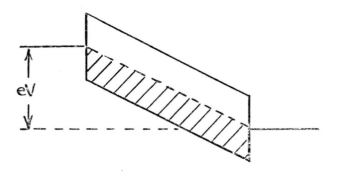

Fig. 1

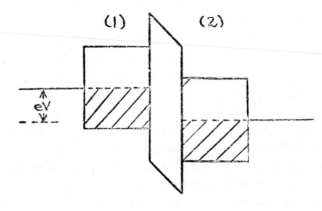

Fig. 2

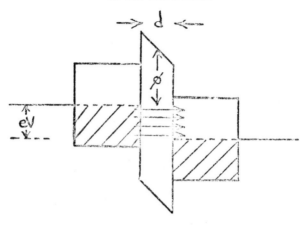

Fig. 3

neling process, only elastic tunneling or scattering
being allowed. In fact, Jacklevic and Lambe[1] showed
that ~1% of the electrons lose energy by exciting vibrations of molecules trapped in the oxide (water, or-
ganic contaminants). As the energy of these vibrations
is typically 100mV-500meV this is not a factor in the
superconductivity studies where the energy range is
0-30meV. However, we found[2] that the electrons can
excite vibrations of the oxide itself (50-100meV) and
also of the surfaces of the metal films (0-30meV).
Fortunately, in typical junctions only ~1% of the tunneling electrons lose energy in this way. If a majority
did so then the measurement of the density of states in
superconductors would be impossible as the electrons
would dribble into metal (2) close to the Fermi level.
The electrons may also interact with magnetic impurities in the oxide layer[3] and it is best to avoid that type
of junction for superconductivity studies as nobody has
thought very hard about what your measurements mean

if an appreciable fraction of the electrons scatter with
spin exchange in the barrier. This problem of scattering in the barrier is a talk on its own so I had better
say no more about it here, except that we have considered the inelastic (nonmagnetic) scattering and correct
for it in the normalization of derivatives when we obtain
the superconducting excitation spectrum.

Let me now change from the density of states representation of the metals (Fig. 4) to a particle representation which I think is much more useful, especially
in superconductivity. We plot the momentum k and
energy ϵ of the electrons assuming the usual parabolic
dependence (Fig. 5). The Fermi level ϵ_F is fixed so
that if we inject an electron into this system the only
allowed states are $\epsilon > \epsilon_F$, if we extract an electron we
are left with a hole with $\epsilon < \epsilon_F$. The velocity of the
electron is $d\epsilon/dk$ which is positive in Fig. 5. The hole
moves in the opposite direction so we make its mass
negative (as $d\epsilon/dk$ is also positive as shown).

Using this diagram we can represent tunneling
between normal metals as in Fig. 6 (considering only
+k). An electron is transferred from k_1 in metal 1
to k_2 in metal 2 with $eV = \epsilon_1 + \epsilon_2$, $0 \leq \epsilon_2 \leq eV$. To calculate the tunneling current we want the matrix element
which connects states k_1 and k_2 where these states are
bare single electron states. (This means the matrix
element can't transfer electrons along with their interactions with the lattice phonons, other electrons, etc.,
i.e., the dressed electron). This is given by [4]

$$|T|^2 = \frac{\hbar}{m} \frac{v_{1x}}{2L_1} \frac{v_{2x}}{2L_2} \tau$$

where v_{1x} is the velocity of the electron normal to the

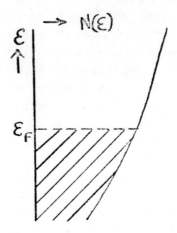

Fig. 4

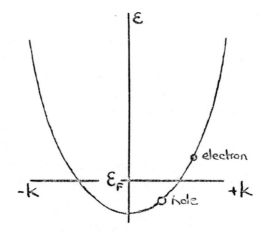

Fig. 5

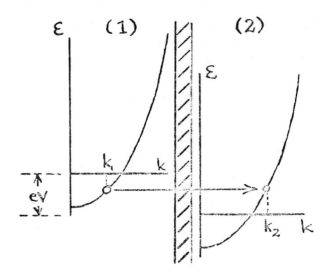

Fig. 6

barrier in 1, L_1 is the thickness of film 1, τ is the transmission probability $\sim\exp(-20)$. If you like I think you can regard $v_{1x}/2L_1$ as the number of times the incident electron reaches the barrier/second, τ its chance of getting through the barrier and $v_{2x}/2L_2$ the number of times the final electron state leaves the barrier each second. The tunneling current is

$$I = \frac{2\pi}{\hbar} \int_0^{eV} |T|^2 (N_1)\ (N_2)\ d\epsilon$$

where N_1 is the density of states in $1 = \frac{L_1}{\pi\hbar v_{1x}}$. You can see that the v_{1x} term from N_1 cancels that in $|T|^2$ so, at least within this simple treatment, the density of states does not appear in tunneling between normal metals.

The assumption that τ is independent of ϵ and k has also been made until fairly recently. In fact if one is studying very small conductance changes in the normal state dI/dV is not independent of V for small voltages (~ 10 mV) as would be expected from the discussion above. The variation in dI/dV arises partly because eV is not negligible compared to the barrier height φ (hence τ varies with ϵ) and partly because of the inelastic scattering discussed earlier.

To get back to the tunneling diagrams, it seems easier to think of the electron and hole as excitations which cost an energy $E = |\epsilon|$ to create. For example an incident photon of energy hν could excite an electron from $-\epsilon_h$ below the Fermi level to ϵ_e above with hν = $\epsilon_h + \epsilon_e$. Thus we create a hole excitation with E_h = $|\epsilon_h|$ and an electron with $E_e = |\epsilon_e|$ and we redraw the picture considering only allowed excitation states, all with positive energy relative to the Fermi level E_F. We have simply created two excitations with $E_e + E_h$ = hν. Now the velocity of the excitation is dE/dk which is positive and negative for the electron and hole respectively.

The tunneling experiment between normal metals is the transfer of an electron from metal 1 to 2, or the creation of a hole in 1 and an electron in 2. This is represented by (considering only +k). Conservation of energy requires eV = $E_{h1} + E_{e2}$ and as there are allowed hole and electron levels immediately above E_{F1} and E_{F2} current will flow as soon as a bias is applied. We obtain the "band" of electrons injected into 2 by remembering that $0 < E_{e2} < eV$ applies in addition to $E_{h1} + E_{e2}$ = eV.

You all know that when one tunnels into a superconductor the density of states does appear directly in

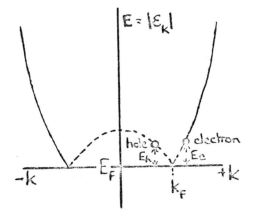

Fig. 7

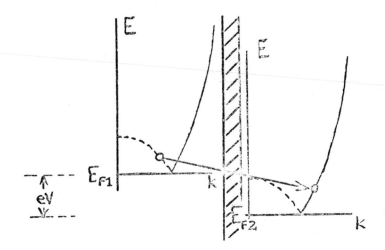

Fig. 8

the tunneling characteristic. I have not seen a satisfy-
ing simple explanation of why this is so but the difference between the tunneling process in normal metals
and superconductors becomes clearer when we consider the kind of excited states into which we try to inject the tunneling electron. In a superconductor we have
this effective attraction between electrons which you
have heard so much about. We can regard this as binding two electrons into Cooper pairs with a binding energy of Δ/electron. This means that at T = 0 °K all the
important electrons near the Fermi level are condensed
into this paired ground state and we have no single particle excitations. To create an excitation you could
shine infra-red radiation on the superconductors, this
would take an energy 2Δ as you have to break up a pair
and create two excitations. But if you injected a single
excitation with a tunneling experiment this would only
cost energy Δ. So as we have no allowed excitations
with energy $< \Delta$ the E vs k diagram should be redrawn
as in Fig. 9. I have shown two electron excitations at
+k and -k, if these had opposite spins they could pair
and disappear into the ground state. This disappearance
of an electron by pairing is equivalent to a scattering
potential which changes electrons into holes. Because
of this scattering the sharp distinction between electrons
for $k > k_F$ and holes with $k < k_F$ in the normal metal
does not hold in the superconductor. Especially for energies just above Δ it is possible to place an electron
in a state with $k < k_F$. The energy of these excitations
is not $E = |\epsilon|$ as in the normal metal but

$$E = \sqrt{\epsilon^2 + \Delta^2}$$

Selecting the particle at k we can think of it as being an

electron for part of the time

$$\text{given by } u_k^2 = 1/2 \left(1 + \frac{\epsilon_K}{E_K}\right)$$

and as a hole for the rest of the time

$$v_k^2 = 1 - u_k^2 = 1/2 \left(1 - \frac{\epsilon_K}{E_K}\right)$$

If this k corresponds to an energy $E = 2\Delta$ then $\epsilon = \Delta\sqrt{3}$ and the excitation is an electron for

$$1/2 \left(1 + \frac{\Delta\sqrt{3}}{2\Delta}\right) = .93$$

of the time and a hole for .07 of the time. Conversely in Fig. 10 the particle at k" is a hole for .93 of the time. As E increases above Δ the distinction between the electron and hole nature of the excitations becomes closer to the normal metal case.

Now the tunneling matrix element $|T|^2$ transfers only electrons across the barrier, not these peculiar electron-hole quasiparticles. So if we want to inject an electron at energy 2Δ with a tunneling experiment we must put it partly above and partly below k_F in the proportion .93 to .07. If one is interested in the possible density of states for injection of this electron it is equally well given by putting the electron completely in one branch ($k' > k_F$ say). In the normal metal the density of states is $N(0) = dk/d\epsilon$ and the simplest answer for the superconductor is

$$N(E) = \frac{dk}{dE} = \frac{E}{\sqrt{E^2 - \Delta^2}} \frac{dk}{d\epsilon} = N(0) \frac{E}{\sqrt{E^2 - \Delta^2}}$$

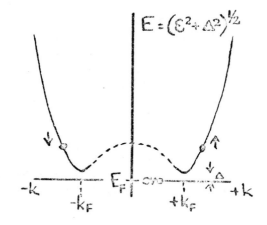

Fig. 9

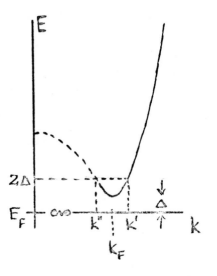

Fig. 10

This, if you like, is the normal density of states $N(0)$ modified by the square root singularity

$$\frac{E}{\sqrt{E^2 - \Delta^2}}$$

produced by superconductivity. Going back to the expression for the tunneling current you will see that if we take the derivative dI/dV of the tunneling characteristic then

$$\frac{dI}{dV}_S \bigg/ \frac{dI}{dV}_N = \frac{E}{\sqrt{E^2 - \Delta^2}}$$

The experimental result for Sn, In and Al is very close to this behavior but Pb and Hg have quite strong deviations. These result from the strong electron-phonon interactions, occurring especially at energies where the density of phonons is large. The interaction therefore varies with energy instead of being constant (out to a cutoff energy) as assumed by BCS, and gives rise to a complex energy dependent gap parameter $\Delta(E)$. The tunneling density of states[5] is now

$$N(0) \, \text{Re} \left\{ \frac{E}{\sqrt{E^2 - \Delta(E)^2}} \right\}$$

and I am afraid I can't derive that result using simple arguments.

Having outlined the main result that will be used in the second half of this talk, namely that a measurement of

for a M-I-S junction is equivalent to determining the
superconducting density of states (if you could do the
experiment at T = 0), let me now illustrate a few
more tunneling experiments using these excitation
diagrams.

Tunneling between a metal and superconductor
(at T = 0) is represented by Fig. 11 for one bias, or
Fig. 12 when the bias is reversed. In both cases we
create one excitation on each side of the barrier. The
normal metal excitation costs negligible energy but
that in the superconductor requires a minimum ex-
penditure of Δ and no current can flow for voltages
less than eV = Δ. The I-V characteristic of the junction looks like Fig. 13 and would allow an accurate determination of Δ if T = 0 and no smearing of the onset
at Δ took place. At T $\neq$ 0 you can put a number of excitations at E > Δ and convince yourselves that an appreciable current can flow even for eV $\ll$ Δ.

You may wonder why I am not using the familiar
diagram of Fig. 14, the semiconductor diagram with
"full states below the gap" and "empty states" above.
I believe in some cases this diagram is misleading and
I find it much easier to think of a superconductor (at T
= 0) as having pairs at the Fermi level and excited
states with a minimum Δ above the Fermi level. (Fig.
15). Of course the only electrons available for tunneling are those which result from breaking a pair. In
all these figures we grossly exaggerate Δ compared to
E_F, in practice the normal metal density of states is
essentially constant near the Fermi level.

A simple illustration of the difference in the
physics behind the two diagrams is shown in Fig. 16
where infra-red absorption is taking place. In the
seimconductor diagram we create an electron-hole

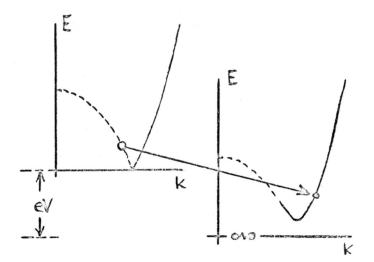

Fig. 11

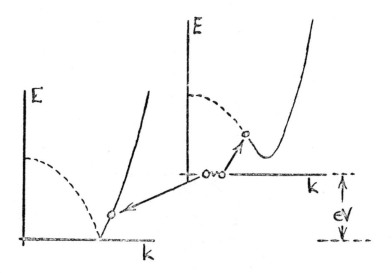

Fig. 12

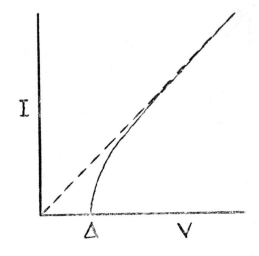

Fig. 13

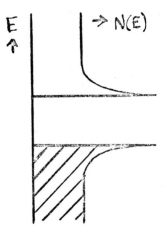

Fig. 14

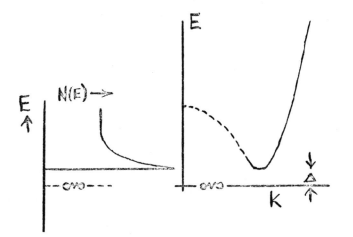

Fig. 15

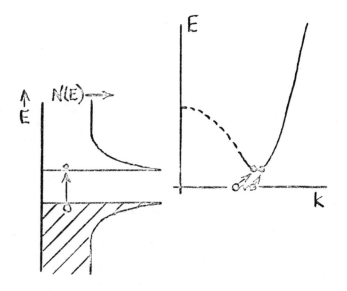

Fig. 16

pair (costing energy 2Δ) and at a later time allow
these to recombine. This is apparently independent
of the number of pairs in the system. In fact the
photon creates two excitations by breaking a Cooper
pair (the superconductor goes from N to N-1 pairs)
and later these may recombine to regain the missing
pair (and emit a phonon of energy 2Δ).

Tunneling between two superconductors takes
place by the destruction of a pair and the appearance
of an excitation in each superconductor (Fig. 17).
The minimum energy required to create these excitations is $\Delta_1 + \Delta_2$ and the I-V characteristic is shown
in Fig. 18.

If you want to include the density of states in
Fig. 17 simply consider what dk/dE is for each of the
excitations. When $eV = \Delta_1 + \Delta_2$, dk/dE is infinite for
both particles and a discontinuous jump in current
should occur at this voltage even at $T \neq 0$ (never observed in practice due to smearing of the gap).

As this Institute is primarily concerned with
magnetic field effects let me describe an experiment
which looks interesting but has not been done very
carefully by anyone. It consists simply of taking a
S-I-S junction to as low a temperature as possible
and measuring the I-V characteristic as a function of
small transverse magnetic field. In zero field the current for $eV < 2\Delta$ should be $\sim \exp(-\Delta/kT)$ which can
be very small for Pb at $1\,^\circ$K, in practice a current
$\sim 10^{-5}$ of the normal state current will be observed.
As field is applied and fluxoids, flux bundles or normal regions of the mixed state enter the films this
current will increase in an interesting way Fig. 19.

If the normal regions of the fluxoids line up opposite to each other across the insulator then a

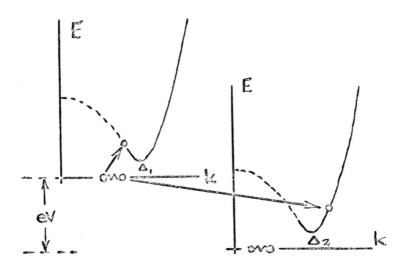

Fig. 17

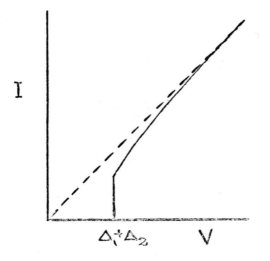

Fig. 18

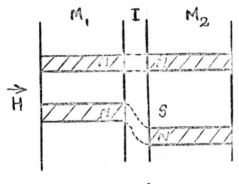

(a)

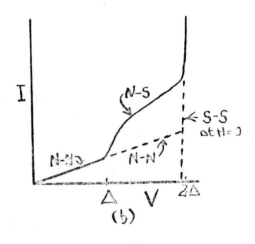

(b)

Fig. 19

current will flow for $0 < eV < 2\Delta$. If the fluxoids do not line up, so that a normal region faces superconductor in the other film, current will flow only for $\Delta < eV < 2\Delta$. By studying the current in these two voltage ranges as a function of field one can in fact decide whether the fluxoids overlap or avoid each other. The evidence so far (from tunneling)[6] is that they avoid each other but I encourage one of you to try the experiment seriously as that is a puzzling result.

A recent novel use of superconducting tunnel junctions due to Eisenmenger and Dayem[7] is as generators of phonons. One may ask the question, if a bias 4Δ is applied to a S-I-S junction how many phonons of energy 2Δ can be emitted by tunneling one electron? The tunneling process is shown in Fig. 20 where a pair in 1 is broken and an excitation appears at Δ in 1 and at 3Δ in 2 (considering the extreme case). The excitation in 2 can emit a phonon of energy 2Δ and reach the gap. It stays at Δ until a particle of equal and opposite spin and momentum is close enough for pairing to occur, in the absence of thermally excited quasiparticles (i.e., $T = 0$) it presumably waits forever. At $T \neq 0$ pairing occurs and a 2Δ phonon is emitted. The particle in 1 also waits a similar time and by pairing with a thermal excitation emits a phonon 2Δ. Thus three 2Δ phonons are emitted as long as $T \neq 0$. (One should note that the thermal excitations would eventually pair with other thermal excitations to emit 2Δ phonons which in turn break pairs. This is a continuous process which is not observed with the detector junction. The phonons due to the tunneling process are observed once they escape from the films of the generator junction.)

Two rather different tunneling processes from those discussed above, both of which involve simulta-

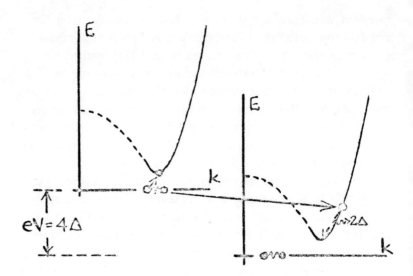

Fig. 20

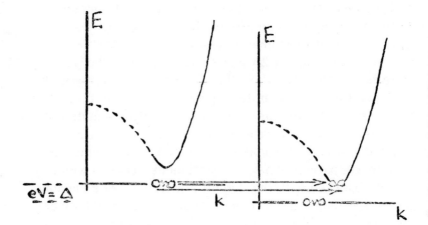

Fig. 21

neous tunneling of two electrons, are multiparticle[8] and Josephson tunneling.[9] In the multiparticle process (Fig. 21) a pair in 1 is broken but both excitations appear in 2. By equating energies one can see that this can occur for $eV \geq \Delta$. As this transfer is a $|T|^4$ process it is expected to be weak compared to the normal state tunneling current $|T|^2$. Josephson tunneling (Fig. 22) is the transfer of a pair from 1 to 2 without any excitations appearing in either film. This requires no energy and occurs at $V = 0$ as in bulk superconductors.

Finally, as an illustration of an experiment which you can't understand without using these excitation diagrams, let me mention the interference effects observed in S-N proximity films. Considering first a single normal metal film, an electron injected at +k travels across the film (assuming the mean free path > thickness of the film d) and is reflected as an electron -k. When this electron reaches the front surface of the film again (as a wave e^{-ikx}) it can interfere with the injected wave (e^{+ikx}) to give an interference term $\cos(2kd)$. As k_F is large compared to typical injection momenta ($k-k_F$) the period of the oscillation is roughly $2k = 2k_F$ which corresponds to ~ 3 Å. Thus in order to see these oscillations (say in $N(0)$) the film would have to be uniform to one atomic layer. This impossible limit on uniformity does not apply to a superconducting film however. Consider only the k' part of an electron injected at E into a superconductor backed by a normal metal. The superconductor-normal metal interface produces a local variation in the BCS scattering potential. The k' particle is scattered into the k" particle by this varying potential and travels back to the front surface of the film. (The normal metal can be regarded as a source of single electrons and the scattering as a process where the in-

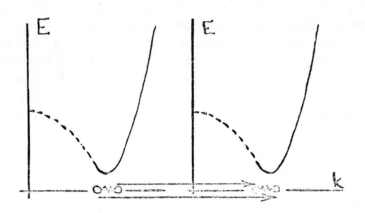

Fig. 22

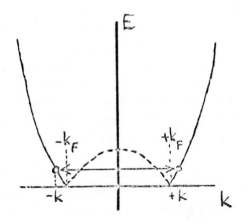

Fig. 23

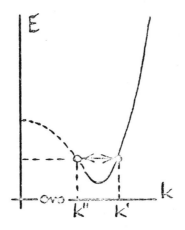

Fig. 24

coming electron k' pairs with one of these normal electrons to disappear as a Cooper pair, which produces the hole at k".) Interference again occurs at the injecting surface but the period is $\cos(k' - k'')d$. As $k' - k''$ is very much less than k_F for injection at $E \gtrsim \Delta$ this interference is easily observed in relatively thick films as long as the mean free path is sufficiently long. This interference was observed as a series of oscillations in the density of states by Tomasch[10,11] and is now known as the Tomasch effect. A similar interference[12] can be produced by injecting electrons into a normal metal which is backed by a superconductor but the magnitude of the density of state effects is considerably smaller.

I hope this has served as a simple introduction to the second lecture. If it has made you think in terms of pairs and excitations instead of electrons and holes in superconductors then its point has been well taken.

REFERENCES

1. R. C. Jaklevic and J. Lambe, Phys. Rev. Letters 17, 1139 (1966).

2. J. M. Rowell and W. L. McMillan, Bull. Am. Phys. Soc. 12, 77 (1967).

3. J. Appelbaum, Phys. Rev. 154, 633 (1967); L. Y. L. Shen and J. M. Rowell, Phys. Rev. 165, 566 (1968).

4. W. A. Harrison, Phys. Rev. 123, 85 (1961).

5. D. J. Scalapino, J. R. Schrieffer and J. W. Wilkins, Phys. Rev. 148, 263 (1966).

6. C. J. Adkins, Phil. Mag. 8, 1051 (1963).

7. W. Eisenmenger and A. H. Dayem, Phys. Rev. Letters 18, 125 (1967).

8. J. R. Schrieffer and J. W. Wilkins, Phys. Rev. Letters 10, 17 (1963).

9. B. D. Josephson, Phys. Letters 1, 251 (1962).

10. W. J. Tomasch, Phys. Rev. Letters 15, 672 (1965).

11. W. L. McMillan and P. W. Anderson, Phys. Rev. Letters 16, 85 (1966).

12. J. M. Rowell and W. L. McMillan, Phys. Rev.
Letters 16, 453 (1966).

RELAXATION OF THE COOPER PAIR DENSITY

A. Schmid

RELAXATION OF THE COOPER PAIR DENSITY

A. Schmid
Department of Physics
University of Karlsruhe, West Germany

The problem I want to talk of is part of a whole family of non-equilibrium processes in superconductors where the Cooper pair density changes in time.

I. For general orientation, let us first consider two other members of this family

i) Vortex motion in the resistive state (Kim et al[1]). (See Fig. 1.) I emphasize that no direct motion of pairs is associated with the motion of the vortex. On the left side, pairs are formed and on the right side pairs are destroyed.

ii) Response of a superconducting thin film to an alternating electrical field in the case where a d. c. current is already present (Rosenblum et al[2]). In a superconductor, the pair density decreases with increasing velocity of the pairs (pair breaking). Since the pair velocity changes in time according to

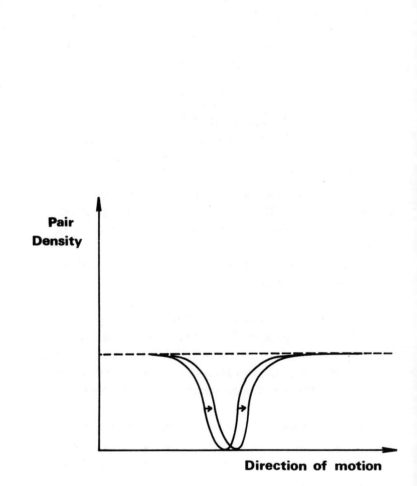

Fig. 1. The pair density in a section of a
vortex line at two consecutive times.

$$M\frac{\partial \vec{v}_s}{\partial t} = - e \vec{E}_\sim,\qquad(\text{I}.1)$$

the problem is whether the pair density is able to respond to the quick changes of the velocity or whether it assumes a constant value corresponding to the mean velocity. (See Fig. 2.) Introducing a relaxation time τ_R, we may characterize the first (second) case by the inequality $\omega \ll 1/\tau_R$ ($\omega \gg 1/\tau_R$), where ω is the frequency of the alternating field. In the Ginzburg-Landau limit, we have

$$\vec{j} = - \frac{e\,|\alpha|}{\beta}\left(1 - \frac{mv_s^2}{2|\alpha|}\right)\vec{v}_s\qquad(\text{I}.2)$$

From this we conclude that the induced a.c. current density is given by

$$\vec{j}_\sim = \frac{e^2\,|\alpha|}{m\,\omega\beta}\left(1 - \frac{n\,mv_0}{2\,|\alpha|}\right)(-i\,\vec{E}_\sim)\qquad(\text{I}.3)$$

where

$$n = \begin{cases} 3, & \text{if} \quad \omega \ll 1/\tau_R; \\ 1, & \text{if} \quad \omega \gg 1/\tau_R. \end{cases}$$

iii) I present you now, that member of the above mentioned family which I studied more in detail.[3] Consider a spatially homogeneous and isotropic superconductor (without impurities) where a small deviation of the Cooper pair density from

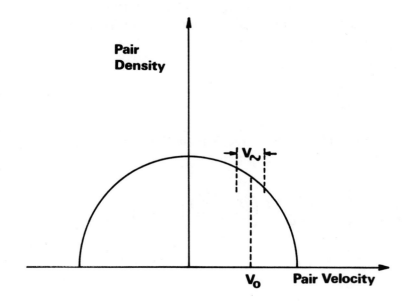

Fig. 2. V_0 is the mean value of the pair
velocity and $v_\sim$ the alternating part of it.

its equilibrium value has been set up initially
(say, by heating or electromagnetic fields).
This deviation will decay in time

$$e^{-t/\tau_R},$$

where τ_R is the relaxation time of this process
and I will show how to calculate τ_R.
Almost the same problem, namely the relaxation of the order parameter (the square of which
is proportional to the pair density) has been
treated by Lucas and Stephen[4] and by Woo and
Abrahams[5] with different results. This problem is closely related to (ii), except that thin
films will have many impurities and that there
is a nonvanishing super current in the equilibrium state. In some sense, it is even possible
to find a connection between the present problem
and (i).

II.   According to a well known result of the BCS
theory,[6] an energy 2Δ is required in order to break
up Cooper pairs in single electrons. Furthermore,
the number of pairs can only be changed by an external perturbation of frequency $\hbar\omega > 2\Delta$. This is
due to an approximation in this theory where only
those collisions between two electrons are considered
which give rise to the formation of bound pairs. Consequently, it is short of a mechanism by which thermodynamic equilibrium with various numbers of pair
densities can be established.

    Let us now consider a collision of a phonon or an
excited electron with a Cooper pair. You may convince yourself easily that the energy necessary to

break up this pair can be furnished by the colliding particle. Of course, there are processes in the reverse direction where pairs are formed so that in equilibrium, no net change in the number of Cooper pairs occurs. As far as this point is concerned, the siutation is analogous to the chemical equilibrium in the gaseous mixture of atoms and their molecules, say H and H_2.

In order to fix your ideas, I want to remark that the electronic collision time τ_c (for electrons on the Fermi surface) is very large even in the normal state of the metals at the low temperatures considered here ($T \approx 10°K$): It is of the order 10^{-8} sec for both electron-phonon and electron-electron collisions (one has $\theta^2/T^2 . \hbar/kT$ and $E_F/kT . \hbar/kT$ respectively), and the corresponding mean free path is of the order 1 cm. It is clear that $\tau_R > \tau_c$, which means that the relaxation of the pair density is a fairly slow process.

III. For methodological reasons, I will not immediately carry through the programme outlined above but consider the normal state for temperatures $T > T_c$. Here, the equilibrium pair density is zero and there is no energy gap. If, by a chance, initially the pair density is different from zero, it will decay. Since there is no energy gap, no triple collisions as described above are needed and the spontaneous decay of the pairs determines the relaxation time τ_R. This allows one to start from the Gorkov equation.[9] We use temperature dependent Green's function in Nambu's matrix notation

$$\hat{G}(x, x') = - \begin{pmatrix} \langle T\psi_\uparrow(x)\psi_\uparrow(x') \rangle & \langle T\psi_\uparrow(x)\psi_\downarrow(x') \rangle \\ \\ \langle T\overline{\psi}_\downarrow(x)\overline{\psi}_\uparrow(x') \rangle & {}_- \langle T\psi_\downarrow(x')\overline{\psi}_\downarrow(x) \rangle \end{pmatrix} ;$$

$$x = (\vec{r}; \tau), \quad x' = (\vec{r}; \tau') \tag{III.1}$$

which satisfy the equation of motion

$$\left\{ -\frac{\partial}{\partial \tau}\,\hat{1} + \left(\frac{1}{2m}\,\nabla^2 + E_F\right)\hat{\tau}_3 - \Delta\hat{\tau}_1 \right\}\hat{G} = \hat{1} \tag{III.2}$$

where Δ is given by the self consistency relation

$$\Delta(x) = - g\, G_{12}(x, x) \tag{III.3}$$

(τ_j are Pauli matrices; $k = \hbar = 1$)

We put $\hat{G} = \hat{G}^{(0)} + \delta\hat{G}$ and $\Delta = \Delta^{(0)} + \delta\Delta$, where the superscript (0) denotes the equilibrium quantities. In the present case, we have $\Delta^{(0)} = 0$ and

$$(\hat{G}^{(0)})^{-1} = \left\{ -\frac{\partial}{\partial t}\,\hat{1} + \left(\frac{1}{2m}\,\nabla^2 + E_F\right)\hat{\tau}_3 \right\}$$

From this we obtain the linearized equation

$$(\hat{G}^{(0)})^{-1}\,\delta\hat{G} - \delta\Delta\,\hat{\tau}_i\,\hat{G}^{(0)} = 0 ; \tag{III.4}$$

or

$$\delta\hat{G} = \hat{G}^{(0)}\,\delta\Delta\,\hat{\tau}_1\,\hat{G}^{(0)} . \tag{III.5}$$

Taking the (12) matrix element of this equation and using the self consistency relation we arrive at

$$\delta\Delta(\vec{r};\tau) = -g \int_0^{1/T} d\tau' \int d^3r' \, G_{11}^{(0)}(\vec{r} - \vec{r'}; \tau - \tau')$$

(III. 6)

$$G_{22}^{(0)}(\vec{r'} - \vec{r}, \tau' - \tau) \, \delta\Delta(\vec{r'};\tau')$$

In frequency and momentum space this relation becomes

$$\mu(\vec{k}; \omega_n) \, \delta\Delta(\vec{k}; \omega_n) = 0;$$

$$\mu(\vec{k}; \omega_n) = 1 + gT \sum_{\omega_\nu} \int \frac{d^3p}{(2\pi)^3} \, G_{11}^{(0)};(\vec{p};\omega_\nu)$$

$$G_{22}^{(0)}(\vec{p} - \vec{k}; \omega_\nu - \omega_n)$$

(III. 7)

ω_n and ω_ν are even and odd Matsubara frequencies.

This homogeneous equation has only the trivial solution $\delta\Delta = 0$ which means that the equilibrium state is stable. However, if one constructs the analytical continuation of this equation in the region Re $\omega_n > 0$, and puts $\omega_n = -i\Omega$ one finds solutions for some Ω_0 in the lower complex Ω half-plane.[10] Since the time dependence of these solutions is $\sim e^{-i\Omega_0 t}$, they decay with a decay time Im $1/\Omega_0$. Considering that the pair density is proportional to Δ^2, we obtain the relaxation time

$$\tau_R = \frac{1}{2} \, \text{Im} \, \frac{1}{\Omega_0} \quad (T > T_c)$$

(III. 8)

For the problem of interest here, it is sufficient

to insert the Green's function of the ideal Fermi gas. It is possible to expand μ in powers of Ω and V_0k (V_0: Fermi velocity) if both quantities are smaller than πT. In the lowest non-trivial order one obtains

$$\mu(k, \omega_n = -i\Omega) = g N_0 \left\{ \frac{T - T_c}{T_c} + \frac{\sigma_3}{6} \frac{V_0^2 k^2}{\pi^2 T_c^2} - \frac{i\pi \Omega}{8T_c} \right\} \;;$$

$$\sigma_3 = \sum_{\nu \geq 0} \frac{1}{(2\nu + 1)^3} = \frac{7}{8} \zeta(3), \qquad (\text{III.9})$$

from where we find the relaxation time

$$\tau_R = \frac{\pi}{16T_c} \frac{1}{(T - T_c)/T_c + \frac{1}{6}\sigma_3 (V_0 k)^2/(\pi T_c)^2}$$

$$(\text{III.10})$$

If one were to try the same method for $T < T_c$, i.e., $\Delta^{(0)} \neq 0$, one would find the following generalization of equation (III.7)

$$\mu(\vec{k}, \omega_n) = 1 + g T \sum_{\omega_\nu} \int \frac{d^3 p}{(2\pi)^3} \left\{ G_{11}^{(0)}(\vec{p}; \omega_\nu) \right.$$

$$G_{22}^{(0)}(\vec{p} - \vec{k}; \omega_\nu - \omega_n)$$

$$\left. + G_{12}^{(0)}(\vec{p}; \omega_\nu) G_{12}^{(0)}(\vec{p} - \vec{k}; \omega_\nu - \omega_n) \right\} \qquad (\text{III.11})$$

For simplicity, we consider the case $k = 0$, where

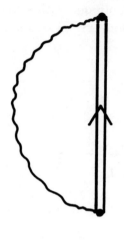

Fig. 3

$$\mu \, (0, \omega_n = -i\Omega) = 2 \, \frac{T_c - T}{T_c} \, (1 - \frac{\Omega^2}{4\Delta^2}) \, - \frac{\pi \, i}{8T_c} \, \sqrt{\Omega^2 - 4\Delta^2}$$

$$(\text{III}.12)$$

This expression has zeros (and branching points) at $\Omega = \pm \, 2\Delta$, i.e., there is no decay.[11]

IV. I want to show now that the relaxation time τ_R of the pair density is given by the zeros of $\mu(\vec{k}, \omega_n = i\Omega)$ in eq. (III.11), where, however, one has to insert the correct equilibrium Green's functions which include collisions. The accuracy of the results obtained thus, is of the order T_c/θ in the case of electron-phonon collisions (θ: Debye temperature) and of the order T_c/E_F in the case of electron-electron collisions (E_F: Fermi energy), provided $|\Omega| \ll T_c$.

Let us now study in detail the interaction of electrons and phonons. According to Eliashberg,[12] the Green's function $\hat{G}$, (eq. (III.1)), and the corresponding self-energy Σ satisfy the equation

$$\sum_{jk} (x, x') = - \eta_{jk} \, D(x - x') \, G_{jk}(x, x');$$

$$\eta_{jk} = \begin{cases} +1 & \text{if } j = k \\ -1 & \text{if } j \neq k \end{cases}$$

$D(x - x')$ is here the Green's function of the phonons. It is little affected by the transition in the superconductive state,[12] which means particularly that we can take the equilibrium Green's function or even the Green's function of non-interacting phonons is sufficient for our purpose.

In terms of Feynman graphs, the above equation is represented in Fig. 3.

It has been realized, [12] that only those Fourier components with respect to the difference r - r' of the space coordinates are important which have momenta close to the Fermi momentum p_0 and that in this region they do not depend on the momentum. This allows us to write eq. (IV. 2) in the form

$$\sum_{jk} (\vec{R}; \tau, \tau') = - \eta_{jk} B(\tau - \tau') G_{jk}(\vec{R}, \vec{R}; \tau, \tau');$$

$$\text{(IV.2)}$$

where

$$\vec{R} = \frac{1}{2}(r + r')$$

is the centre of mass coordinate (of the Cooper pairs). For convenience, we give $B(\tau)$ by its Fourier transform

$$B(\omega_n) = \frac{1}{2p_0} \int_0^{2p_0} dk \, k \, D(\vec{k}; \omega_n)$$

$$\approx g^2 \left[1 - \frac{\omega_n^2}{\theta^2} \ln\left(1 + \frac{\omega_n^2}{\theta^2}\right) \right]$$

$$\text{(IV.3)}$$

The last expression corresponds to the Debye model. We draw attention to the fact that $B(\omega_n)$ is a smooth function of ω_n and that its fractional change is approximately ω_n^2/θ^2. [13] For a small change $\delta\hat{\Sigma}$, we have

$$\delta \hat{G} = \hat{G}^{(0)} \delta \sum \hat{G}^{(0)}$$

or

$$\delta \hat{\sum} = \eta B \hat{G}^{(0)} \delta \hat{\sum} \hat{G}^{(0)} \qquad \text{(IV.4)}$$

We consider the case where

$$\delta \sum_{12} = \delta \sum_{21} = \sum_{12} - \overset{(0)}{\sum_{12}} = \phi .$$

In frequency and momentum space, eq. (IV.4) now becomes

$$\phi_{\vec{k}}(\omega_\nu, \omega_{\nu'}) = T \sum_{\omega_n} B(\omega_n) M_{\vec{k}}(\omega_\nu + \omega_n, \omega_{\nu''} + \omega_n) \qquad \text{(IV.5)}$$

$$\phi_{\vec{k}}(\omega_\nu + \omega_n, \omega_{\nu'} + \omega_n)$$

where $\phi_{\vec{k}}$ oscillates

$$\sim e^{i\vec{k}.\vec{R}} e^{i\omega_\nu \tau - i\omega_{\nu'}\tau'}$$

and

$$M_{\vec{k}}(\omega_\nu, \omega_{\nu'}) = \int \frac{d^3p}{(2\pi)^3} \left\{ G_{11}^{(0)}(\vec{p}; \omega_\nu) G_{22}^{(0)}(\vec{p} - \vec{k}; \omega_{\nu'}) \right.$$

$$\left. + G_{12}^{(0)}(\vec{p}; \omega_\nu) G_{12}^{(0)}(\vec{p} - \vec{k}; \omega_{\nu'}) \right\} \qquad \text{(IV.6)}$$

We recall that $\hat{G}^{(0)}$ is of the form

$$G^{(0)}(\epsilon_{\vec{k}}, \omega_\nu) = - \frac{i\omega_\nu Z^{(0)}(\omega_\nu) 1 + \epsilon \tau_3 + \sum_{12}^{(0)}(\omega_\nu) \tau_1}{[\omega_\nu Z^{(0)}(\omega_\nu)]^2 + \epsilon^2 + [\sum_{12}^{(0)}(\omega_\nu)]^2} ; \qquad \text{(IV.7)}$$

and that $z^{(0)}$ and $\Sigma_{12}^{(0)}$ are even functions of ω_ν. In the following, the analytical continuation of $\hat{G}^{(0)}$ and $\hat{\Sigma}^{(0)}$ in the region $\mathrm{Re}\,\omega_\nu > 0$ and for values $|\omega_\nu| \lesssim T$ will be needed. In this case,

$$\omega_\nu z^{(0)}(\omega_\nu) = \omega_\nu + i \sum_{11}^{(0)}(\omega_\nu) = a(\omega_\nu + \frac{1}{\tau_c});$$

$$\sum_{12}^{(0)}(\omega_\nu) = a\,\Delta; \qquad\qquad\qquad (\text{IV.8})$$

where a is a constant of the order unity, $\tau_c \approx \theta^2/T^3$ is the life-time of electrons due to collisions with phonons[14] (we have dropped the superscript '0' on the equilibrium value of the energy gap Δ).

It is necessary to carry out the analytical continuation of eq. (IV.5) into the region of real frequencies in order to be able to introduce the "centre of mass" $-i\Omega = \omega_\nu - \omega_{\nu'}$ and the internal frequency $-i\omega = 1/2\,(\omega_\nu + \omega_{\nu'})$. A consistent assumption on the analytical behaviour of

$$\phi_{\vec{k}}(\omega_\nu, \omega_{\nu'})$$

is that this quantity has only singularities at $\mathrm{Re}\,\omega_\nu = 0$; $\mathrm{Re}\,\omega_{\nu'} = 0$; and $\mathrm{Re}\,(\omega_\nu - \omega_{\nu'}) = 0$. Writing in eq. (IV.5)

$$T \sum_{\omega_n} \cdots = \frac{1}{4\pi} \int_c dz \frac{iz}{2T} \cdots,$$

we arrive at the desired analytical continuation. (See Fig. 4.)

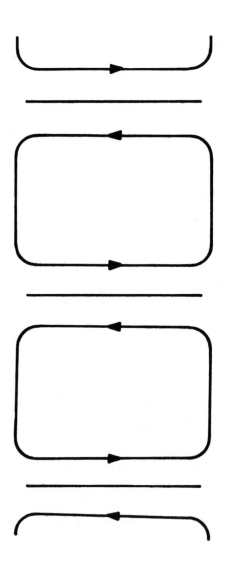

Fig. 4. The contour C of the complex integration.

I do not want to go more into detail. As far as the general procedure is concerned, I have to mention that eq. (IV.5) has a solution for $\omega_\nu = \omega_{\nu'}$ if $k = 0$ and $T = T_c$. This is a consequence of the fact that at T_c there is a second order phase transition. This particular solution can be used as a trial function and one is able to show that eq. (IV.5) is satisfied except of terms of the relative order T_c/θ, provided that $|\Omega| \lesssim T_c$. Thereby, it is essential to realize that the frequency dependence of $\phi(\omega_\nu, \omega_{\nu'} = \omega_\nu)$ is governed by the variation of the function $B(\omega_n)$ which means that the fractional change of ϕ is of the order $(\omega_\nu/\theta)^2$, too. (In the immediate neighbourhood of T_c, the accuracy is even better). In this way we are led to the results which I quoted in the beginning of this section, namely that one has only to insert the Green's function (IV.7) in eq. (III.11). The zeros of this redefined μ in the lower complex Ω half-plane determine the relaxation time τ_R, which, in view of the fact that $\delta\rho_s \sim \Delta\delta\phi$, is given by

$$\tau_R = \text{Im} \ \frac{1}{\Omega_0} \ ; \quad (T < T_c). \qquad \text{(IV.9)}$$

V. I will discuss briefly electron-electron scattering via the screened Coulomb interaction. Remember that I took the electron-phonon interaction into account by considering only the contribution of a Hartree-Fock type diagram to the self-energy. In the case of screened Coulomb interaction, these diagrams are unimportant; one has to take the next order terms into account (Born collision approximation).[15] (See Fig. 5.).

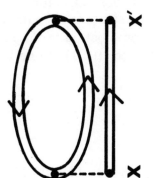

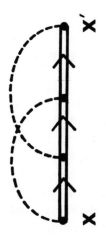

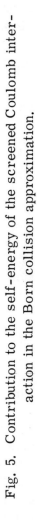

Fig. 5. Contribution to the self-energy of the screened Coulomb interaction in the Born collision approximation.

We consider the screened Coulomb interaction as very short ranged and instantaneous with a coupling constant g_{sc}. This contribution to the self-energy can be incorporated in eq. (IV.1) if one replaces

$$\eta_{ik} D(x - x') \rightarrow \eta_{ik} D(x - x') + \eta_{ik} D_{sc}(x - x') \quad \text{(V.1)}$$

where

$$D_{sc}(x - x') = g_{sc}^2 \{ G_{11}^{(0)}(x - x') G_{11}^{(0)}(x' - x)$$

$$+ G_{12}^{(0)}(x - x') G_{12}^{(0)}(x' - x) \} \quad \text{(V.2)}$$

If we insert the normal state Green's function in eq. (V.2), we get an approximate expression for the function $B_{sc}(\omega_n)$ (cf. eq. (IV.3))

$$B_{sc}(\omega_n) \approx - \frac{16 \, g_{sc}^2 \, N_0 \, E_F^2}{\omega_n^2 + 4\pi \, E_F \, |\omega_n| + 16 \, E_F^2} \quad \text{(V.3)}$$

This term increases the collision time τ_c of the electrons by a contribution of the order E_F/T^2, which is numerically of the same order as the phonon contribution.

The fractional change of B_{sc} is of the form ω_n/E_F as compared to the change ω_n^2/θ^2 of B. As a consequence, all the arguments which led to the solution in sec. IV remain correct if we replace T_c/θ by T_c/E_F. Since this new quantity is of the same order of magnitude as the old ones, nothing is changed in the quality of the approximation.

VI. Since the collision time is infinite at zero temperature, no differences arise in the present treatment compared to the results of Bogolyubov and Anderson.[16]

Thus we are led to consider the region below the transition temperature, i.e. $\Delta < T$. The additional advantage is that we can neglect terms

$$\sim (\Delta/T_c)^4, \quad \sim (v_0 k/T_c)^4.$$

We also neglect term $\sim (\Omega/T_c)^2$ since we will find $|\Omega| \ll T_c$.

We will distinguish the cases

$$v_0 k \underset{>}{\overset{<}{{}}} 2/\tau_c.$$

A) $v_0 k < 2/\tau_c$. Here, we have[17]

$$\mu(k, \omega_n = -i\Omega) = gN_0 \Big\{ \sigma_3 \frac{3\Delta^2 + \frac{1}{6} v_0^2 k^2}{\pi^2 T_c^2} - \frac{T_c - T}{T_c}$$

$$- \frac{i\pi\Omega}{8(2/\tau_c - i\Omega)} \Big[\frac{\sqrt{4\Delta^2 + (2/\tau_c - i\Omega)^2}}{T_c}$$

$$+ \frac{16\Delta^2}{\pi^3 T_c^2} \Big] \Big\} \tag{VI.1}$$

α) If $\Delta < 2/\tau_c$, we have a gap-less superconductor since the energy gap is smaller than the collision broadening of the energy levels. We have in sufficient approximation

$$\mu = gN_0 \left\{ \sigma_3 \frac{3\Delta^2 + \frac{1}{6} v_0^2 k^2}{\pi^2 T_c^2} - \frac{T_c - T}{T_c} - \frac{i\pi \Omega}{8T_c} \right\} \quad (VI.2)$$

If $\Delta = 0$, this μ coincides with the μ we obtained for $T > T_c$ (eq. (III.9)). This allows us to consider the spontaneous decay of Cooper pairs responsible for relaxation here, too. Upon replacing $-i\Omega$ by the time derivative $\partial/\partial t$, eq. (VI. 2) is equivalent to the ansatz made by me earlier in a paper on the resistive state.[18] In a spatially homogeneous clean superconductor as considered here, this ansatz is valid only in a small temperature range close to the transition temperature i.e. $(T_c - T)/T_c \lesssim 10^{-3}$. One might argue, however, that in the Abrikosov mixed state a Cooper pair will find it not difficult to decay spontaneously if it is in the vicinity of a vortex core. This makes it likely that this ansatz (and its generalization in order to include electromagnetic fields) is valid in the mixed state even for lower temperatures and offers an explanation of the good results concerning the resistive state.[19]

β)   If $\Delta > 2/\tau_c$, collisions are responsible for the formation and dissociation of the pairs as described in sec. II. We have here

$$\mu \approx gN_0 \left\{ 2 \frac{T_c - T}{T_c} - \frac{i\pi\Omega}{8} \frac{\Delta}{T_c} \tau_c \right\} \quad (VI.3)$$

where the BCS relation $(T_c - T)/T_c = \sigma_3 \Delta^2/(\pi T_c)^2$ has been used. We obtain the following result for the relaxation time

$$\tau_R = \frac{\pi}{16 T_c} \frac{1}{|T_c - T|/T_c + \frac{1}{6} \sigma_3 v_0^2 k^2 /(\pi T_c)^2}$$

$$\text{if } \Delta < \frac{2}{\tau_c} \qquad (VI.4)$$

$$= \frac{\pi^2}{16} \sqrt{\left(\frac{\sigma_3 T_c}{(T_c - T)}\right)} \tau_c \text{ if } \Delta > \frac{2}{\tau_c}$$

We see that $\tau_R > \tau_c$, as it should be. Note that the first line applies even to the case $T > T_c$.
B) $v_0 k \gg 2/\tau_c$ and $\Delta > 2/\tau_c$. One obtains

$$\mu = g N_0 \left\{ \sigma_3 \frac{3\Delta^2 + \frac{1}{6} v_0^2 k^2}{\pi^2 T_c^2} - \frac{i\pi \Omega \Delta}{4 v_0 k T_c} \times \right.$$

$$\times \left[\ln \frac{2 v_0 k}{(2/\tau_c - i\Omega)(1 + \sqrt{1 + v_0^2 k^2/\Delta^2})} \right.$$

$$\left. + \frac{8 \sigma_3 \Delta}{\pi^2 T} \right] \right\} \qquad (VI.5)$$

One can deduce from this expression that the relaxation time shortens if k increases. The limiting value $\tau_R = \tau_c/2$ will be attained exponentially when

$$k > \frac{1}{l_c} \sqrt{\frac{\pi}{\sigma_3}} \sqrt{T_c/(T_c - T)}$$

where l_c the mean free path

$$\tau_R = \tau_c/2; \text{ if } k > \frac{\pi}{\sqrt{\sigma_3}} \frac{1}{l_c} \sqrt{\frac{T_c}{T_c - T}} \qquad (VI.6)$$

$$\text{and } \Delta > 2/\tau_c.$$

This rapid saturation excludes the possibility that a diffusion process is responsible for the relaxation. Let us recall that in equilibrium in half the number of collisions a pair is formed and in the other half a pair is destroyed. On the other hand, the momentum of a Cooper pair is zero (except an uncertainty

$$\sim \frac{1}{l_c} \sqrt{\frac{T_c}{T_c - T}}$$

perhaps); and it is not only zero in the average. This means that there are no collisions which lead to the formation of Cooper pair of finite momentum. Thus, we conclude that, if there are pairs of finite momentum, they will be destroyed in each collision, i.e. the relaxation time is equal to the collision time.

So far, we have only considered the case where the modulus of the order parameter changes and not its phase. If the modulus is constant and the phase changes, we have $\delta \Sigma_{12} = - \delta \Sigma_{21}$, which causes a change in sign in front of the term

$$G_{12}^{(0)} \ G_{12}^{(0)}$$

in eqs. (III.11) and (IV.6). The conclusion of sec. IV, however, remains valid. I do not go into details and quote the results.

A) $v_0 k < 2/\tau_c; \Delta > 1/\tau_c$

$$\tau_R = \frac{6 \Delta^2 \tau_c}{v_0^2 k^2}$$

(VI.7)

B) $v_0 k \quad 2/\tau_c$

$$\tau_R = \frac{3\pi^3}{2\sigma 3} \frac{T_c \Delta}{v_0^3 k^3}$$

(VI.8)

In the last expression, τ_c does not appear which means that collisions are not needed directly for damping (which is here due, presumably, to thermal smearing). However, if one checks the derivation, it becomes clear that this result makes only sense for

$$\tau_R > \frac{\tau_c}{2} .$$

Both results are qualitatively different from that one obtains at zero temperature, where the modes are undamped oscillations of frequency

$$\Omega_0 = \frac{1}{\sqrt{3}} v_0 k. \quad [16]$$

APPENDIX

I want to make here some considerations concerning the collision time τ_c in order to give some feeling

how this quantity may change in the presence of
impurity scattering. As far as the phonon contribution is concerned, we may observe that $1/\tau_c$ is proportional to the number of collisions, and hence, to
the number of excited phonon. This number is proportional to T^3 (if $T < \theta$); which explains the result
$\tau_c = \theta^2/T^3$. This result should hold whether there is
impurity scattering or not. As far as electron-
electron collisions are concerned, we have to con-
cede that here the Pauli exclusion principle plays an
important role. Without this principle, each encounter
of two electrons would lead to a collision, and we
would have a mean free path equal to the average
distance of electrons, i.e. 10^{-8} cm. Consider now a
Fermi gas of temperature T.

   i) It is clear that a scattering process can only
take place if there are unoccupied states, the total
energy of which is equal to the energy of the colliding particles. This implies that only particles in a
shell of the width $\sim kT$ on the Fermi surface are
allowed to scatter. As a consequence, the particle
density is reduced by a factor $kT/E_F \approx 10^{-4}$.

   ii) Consider now two particles of the kT shell
and consider the sphere on which according to momentum conservation, the final states must lie on
opposite sides of a diameter. (See Fig. 6.) According to the principle, that the final states have to be
unoccupied, only in the section of that sphere with
the kT shell, one will find allowed final states. This
decreases the rule of collisions by another factor of
kT/E_F, so that on the whole we have a mean free
path due to electron-electron collisions

$$ l_c \approx \left(\frac{kT}{E_F} \right)^2 \cdot 10^{-8} \text{ cm} \approx 1 \text{ cm.} $$

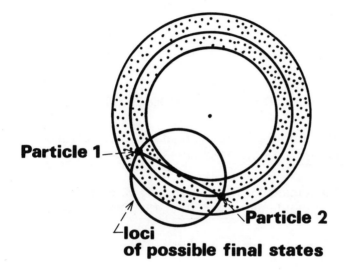

Fig. 6.

In the case where there is scattering of electrons on impurities, energy is still a conserved quantity which means that argument (i) still holds. However, momentum is no longer conserved; and in the case of a very small collision time τ_i with impurities, argument (ii) completely fails. As a consequence, we would expect a mean free path

$$l_c \approx (kT/E_F) \cdot 10^{-8} \text{ cm} \approx 10^{-4} \text{ cm}.$$

REFERENCES AND FOOTNOTES

1. Y. B. Kim, C. F. Hempstead and A. R. Strand: Phys. Rev. 139A, 1163 (1965).

2. J. Gittleman, B. Rosenblum, T. E. Seidel, and A. W. Wicklund: Phys. Rev. 137, A527 (1965).

3. A. Schmid, submitted to Phys. Kondens. Materie.

4. G. Lucas and M. J. Stephen: Phys. Rev. 154, 349 (1967).

5. J. W. F. Woo and E. Abrahams: Phys. Rev. 169, 407, (1968).

6. J. Bardeen, L. N. Cooper and J. R. Schrieffer: Phys. Rev. 108, 1175 (1957).

7. See sec. 21 of ref. 8).

8. Abrikosov, Gorkov and Dzyaloshinskii: Quantum Field Theoretical Methods in Statistical Physics. Pergamon Press (1965). Prentice Hall (1964).

9. See sec. 34 of ref. 8).

10. This is the correct procedure in order to obtain the Fourier transform of the corresponding time-dependent, retarded quantities. See sec. 17 of ref. 8). We remark that the generalized susceptibility corresponding to a perturbation

$$\int d^3 r \, [\, \psi_\uparrow (x) \, \psi_\downarrow (x) + \psi_\downarrow^+ (x) \, \psi_\uparrow^+ (x) \,] \, F(x)$$

is $1/\mu - 1$. It is well known that the modes of a system are determined by the poles of the susceptibilities, i.e., the zeros of μ in the lower half-plane.

11. One may explain this mode as follows: If a Cooper pair were to dissociate spontaneously, it would lack the binding energy 2Δ in the dissociated state. Hence, by the uncertainty relation, it may remain in this state only for a time $\sim 1/2\Delta$. This means that it is forced to oscillate back and forth.

12. G. M. Eliashberg: JETP 11, 696 (1960).

13. This point of view differs from that when you are trying to explain tunneling anomalies by the structure in the phonon density of states. However, one has to remember that in the last case the effects are small.

14. We are referring to the vicinity of the transition temperature, i.e., $\Delta^2/T^2 \ll 1$. The transition to the superconducting state induces practically

no change in the constant a,[12] and the change in $1/\tau_c$ is about Δ^2/T^2. For the values of a and $1/\tau_c$ in the normal state see sec. 21 of ref. 8). For low temperature,

$$\tau_c \approx \theta^2/(\Delta^{3/2} T^{1/2} e^{-\Delta/T})$$

15. Kadanoff and Baym: Quantum Statistical Mechanics. W. A. Benjamin, Inc. (1962), ch 5-3.

16. Bogolyubov, Tolmachev and Shirkov: A New Method in the Theory of Superconductivity. P. W. Anderson: Phys. Rev. 112, 1900 (1958).

17. Note that if $\Omega = 0$, μ is proportional to the second derivative of the Ginzburg-Landau free energy with respect to the order parameter. The reason for this is that both quantities are generalized, static and reciprocal susceptibilities of the same kind.

18. A. Schmid: Phys. Kondens. Materie 5, 302 (1966).

19. cf. C. Caroli and K. Maki: Phys. Rev. 164, 591 (1967).

SIZE EFFECTS IN SUPERCONDUCTORS

E. Guyon

SIZE EFFECTS IN SUPERCONDUCTORS

E. Guyon
Service de Physique des Solides
Laboratoire associé au Centre National
de la Recherche Scientifique
Faculté des Sciences, Orsay, France

A. SUPERCONDUCTING FILMS IN HIGH MAGNETIC FIELDS

I will review some properties of superconducting films related to their size. Films are characterized by their thickness $d_S \sim 50$ to 10^4 Å which is of the order of the two characteristic lengths of superconductors

$\lambda\,(T)$, which says how fast a magnetic field is attenuated in a superconductor

$\xi\,(T)$, which is the characteristic distance for variations of the pair potential $\Delta(r)$

Near the critical temperature T_{cs}, $\lambda\,(T)$ and $\xi\,(T)$ diverge as $(T_{cs} - T)^{-1/2}$. It is possible to observe "thin" films and "thick" film $d \gtrsim \lambda\,(T)$, $\xi\,(T)$ effects on the same system by varying T.

The potential Δ (**r**) diffuses an electron state into a hole state, that is, condenses electrons in pairs

$$\Delta(r) = V < \psi_\uparrow^+ (r)\, \psi_\downarrow^+ (r) > = V\, F\, (r) \qquad (1)$$

$F(r)$ is the amplitude of condensation in pairs ($\psi_\uparrow^+(r)$ creates an electron of spin $\uparrow$ in **r**). V is the electron interaction potential ($V > 0$ for superconductors).

In the limit $|\Delta| \to 0$, the gain in free energy in the superconducting state can be expressed as an expansion in powers of Δ. We write the general expression in the presence of a magnetic field **H** = rot **A**

$$F_s - F_n = A(T)\ |\Delta|^2 + \frac{B}{2}\ |\Delta|^4$$

$$+ \frac{1}{2m}\ |(-i\hbar\nabla - \frac{2e}{c}\,A)\,|\Delta|^2 \qquad (2)$$

The ∇ terms prevent variations of Δ over distances shorter than

$$\xi\, (T) = (\hbar^2/2mA)^{1/2} \qquad (3)$$

The replacement

$$\nabla \to \nabla - \frac{2ie}{\hbar c}\ A \qquad (4)$$

in the presence of a field ensures gauge covariance to Δ defined in (1).

In the Landau picture $A(T) = A_0(T_{cs} - T)$ and B = constant. The Ginzburg-Landau (G.L.) equations which give the equilibrium value of $|\Delta|$ and currents are obtained by minimizing (2) with respect to $|\Delta|$ and **A.**

For a homogeneous superconductor, the equilibrium value $A_0 \neq 0$ for $T < T_{cs}$ and $\Delta_0 = 0$ for $T > T_{cs}$. However it is still reasonable to keep the same form of equation below and above the critical temperature.

This G.L. description can be extended at all temperatures in the sub-critical regime (domain where $|\Delta|$ is small). This situation is met

--for a superconductor penetrated by a high magnetic field

—for a superconductor backed by a normal material near the critical temperature of the sandwich $T_c < T_{cs}$.

We will study these two situations where size effects are important.

I. GENERALIZED G.L. EQUATIONS IN SUPERCONDUCTORS IN THE DIRTY LIMIT

We discuss first the subcritical superconductivity in high magnetic fields in the case where the electron mean free path is small (dirty case).

The G.L. equations were obtained at all temperatures by de Gennes,[2] K. Maki.[3] We will summarize[4] the result of de Gennes

a) Consider first an homogeneous alloy in zero field and in the normal state ($\Delta = 0$) at $T < T_{cs}$.

Δ will grow. As long as there are no saturation effects (Δ small) the growth is exponential.

$$\frac{\partial \Delta}{\partial t} = \frac{\Delta}{\tau_s(T)}$$

The time constant $\tau_s(T)$ was obtained first by Suhl.[5]

--At a temperature T, $\tau_s(T)$ is given by

$$\log\left(\frac{T}{T_{c_s}}\right) = \Psi\left(\frac{1}{2}\right) - \Psi\left(\frac{1}{2} + \frac{\hbar}{4\pi kT \,\tau_s(T)}\right) \qquad (6)$$

Ψ is the digamma function.

--When $T \to T_{c_s}$, $\tau_s(T) \to \infty$. This is characteristic of the long relaxation times near the second order phase transition.

—When $T \to 0$, $\tau_s(T) = \dfrac{\hbar}{\Delta_0(BCS)} = \dfrac{\hbar}{1.75\,T_{c_s}}$.

It is a very short time ($\sim 10^{-11}$ sec).

The variation of $1/\tau_s(T)$ is given in fig. (1) in reduced units.

b) If Δ is a function of position, the equilibrium is reached by an electronic diffusion process. The rate of change of $\Delta(\mathbf{r})$ is given by:

$$\frac{\partial \Delta(\mathbf{r})}{\partial t} = \frac{\Delta(\mathbf{r})}{\tau_s(T)} + D \nabla^2 \Delta(\mathbf{r}) \qquad (7)$$

$D = (1/3)\, V_F\, l$ is the diffusion coefficient for an

electron in the normal state and is obtained from electrical conductivity data.

Let us add a magnetic field. In order to keep gauge covariance, the replacement (4) has to be made:

$$\frac{\partial \Delta(\mathbf{r})}{\partial t} = \frac{\Delta(\mathbf{r})}{\tau_s(T)} + D(\nabla - \frac{2il}{\hbar c} \mathbf{A}(\mathbf{r}))^2 \Delta(\mathbf{r}) \qquad (8)$$

This time dependent equation was derived first by Abrahams and Tsuneto.[6] (See Schmid, same conference.) The G.L. equilibrium solution is given by writing $\partial/\partial t = 0$ in (8).

More precisely the solution can be obtained[2] from the self consistent Gor'kov equation

$$\Delta(\mathbf{r}) = VT \sum_\omega \int H_\omega(\mathbf{r}, \mathbf{r}') \Delta^+(\mathbf{r}') d^3\mathbf{r}',$$

$$\omega = (2n + 1) \pi kT. \qquad (9)$$

The sum is taken over all values of n. The kernel H_ω gives the range of the interaction and is directly related to the correlation function of the positions of an electron in the normal state, $f(\mathbf{r}, \mathbf{r}', t)$

$$\frac{H_\omega(\mathbf{r}, \mathbf{r}')}{N_0} = 2\pi \int_0^\infty f(\mathbf{r}, \mathbf{r}', t) e^{-2|\omega|t/\hbar} dt. \qquad (10)$$

f gives the probability that an electron, introduced at $t = 0$ in $\mathbf{r}$, be in $\mathbf{r}'$ at t. If the mean free path is small, f obeys a diffusion equation

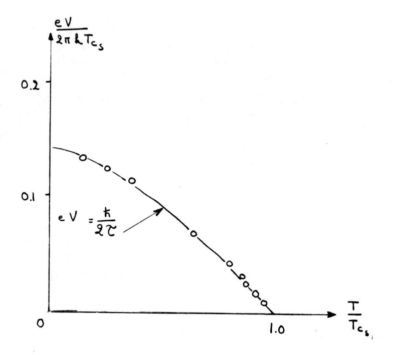

Fig. 1. Temperature dependence of the characteristic time of variation of $\Delta(\mathbf{r})$, $\tau(T)$. The points give the experimental variation of H_{c2} (T) for an Sn In 6% alloy.

$$(\frac{\partial}{\partial t} - D \nabla^2) \, f \, (\mathbf{r}, \, \mathbf{r'} , t) = 0 \qquad (11)$$

with

$$f(\mathbf{r}, \mathbf{r'}, \, 0) = \delta \, (\mathbf{r} - \mathbf{r'}). \qquad (11')$$

The times of interest in (10) are

$$t_1 \sim \frac{\hbar}{2\omega} \sim \frac{\hbar}{2\pi kT} \; .$$

The "dirty limit" expresses that the distance travelled during t_1 must be larger than the mean free path

$$\frac{\hbar V_F}{2\pi \, kT} > 1. \qquad (12)$$

The range of H_ω given from relations (10) and (11) is

$$\xi_\omega = \sqrt{Dt_1} = \sqrt{\frac{\hbar D}{2\omega}} \, . \qquad (13)$$

In the presence of a field, one uses in (11) the replacement given by (4). $\Delta (\mathbf{r})$ is then analyzed in terms of the eigen-functions $u_k(\mathbf{r})$ of the operator

$$-D(\nabla - \frac{2il}{\hbar c} \, \mathbf{A})^2 \, u_k \, (\mathbf{r}) = \epsilon_k (H) \, u_k \, (\mathbf{r}) \qquad (14)$$

By using the solutions for $\Delta(\mathbf{r})$ in the self consistent equation, the linearized G.L. equation with the condition (6) is obtained. Among the solutions of (14), the solution with the smallest eigenvalue $\epsilon_0(H)$ corresponds to the component of fastest growth of $\Delta(\mathbf{r})$ as seen by rewriting (8)

$$\frac{\partial \Delta (\mathbf{r})}{\partial t} = \frac{\Delta(\mathbf{r})}{\tau(T)} - \epsilon_0 (H) \Delta (\mathbf{r}). \qquad (15)$$

At equilibrium

$$\frac{1}{\tau(T)} = \epsilon_0(H). \qquad (16)$$

At the limit of stability of the superconducting state the "natural time for growth of pairs" just compensates the time $1/\epsilon_0(H)$ which expresses the finite lifetime of a pair due to the magnetic interaction that "breaks" the pairs (H acts antisymmetrically on electrons of momentum $\mathbf{p}, -\mathbf{p}$ in the term $\mathbf{P} \cdot \mathbf{A}$).

--In an infinite medium the solution of (14) is that of the harmonic oscillator and the lowest eigenvalue is

$$\epsilon_0(H) = \frac{ehH}{mc} \quad .$$

Using (17), the temperature dependence of the critical field is obtained

$$\frac{e\hbar H_{c2}}{mc} = \frac{1}{\tau(T)} \qquad (18)$$

This relation has been well verified by experiments on thick alloy films in perpendicular geometry (see fig. 1).

The eigenvalue is degenerate: the nucleation at H_{c2} can take place at any point of the superconductor.

However in a semiinfinite superconductor in a field parallel to the surface the nucleation is favoured near it and the upper critical field $H_M = H_{C3} = 1.69\,H_{C2}$ (see talk by Tinkham).

For a thin film with $d \ll \xi$ (T) the nucleation is influenced by the two surfaces. One finds

$$H_M = H_{11} = \sqrt{24}\ \frac{\lambda\,(T)}{d}$$

The interpolation between these two behaviours has been studied in Orsay and will be discussed here.

II. SUBCRITICAL BEHAVIOUR ($H \lesssim H_M$)

The spatial variation of $\Delta\,(\mathbf{r})$ is close to that of the linearized equation for $H = H_M$. However the amplitude of $\Delta\,(\mathbf{r})$ is controlled by the non linear term in the G.L. equation. This term was obtained by Maki,[3] Caroli Cyrot and de Gennes[7] by looking for the next higher order term in the self consistent G.L. equation.

The amplitude of $\Delta(\mathbf{r})$ can be obtained, then, following the scheme used by Abrikosov (see Tinkham, same conference):

a)   For $H < H_M$ the vector potential due to H is $\mathbf{A} = \mathbf{A}_0 + \mathbf{A}_1$. $\mathbf{A}_0$ is the vector potential for a constant field at $\mathbf{H}_M$. $\mathbf{A}_1$ is a correction due to the two effects:
   --the field is smaller than H_M
   --there are supercurrents $\mathbf{J}_s$

b)   In the final expression for Δ the non-linear term $|\Delta|^4$ is replaced by $\beta(|\Delta|^2)^2$. $|\Delta|^2$ will be proportional to $1/\beta$. In the case of a bulk specimen the minimum value of $\beta = 1,16$ (which corresponds to the larger $|\Delta|^2$ and gives the most stable solution) is obtained for a triangular array of vortices.

c) $|\Delta|^2$ is proportional to $(H_M - H)$. This is characteristic of the second order transition in a field. The proportionality factor

$$\frac{|\Delta|^2}{H_M - H}$$

expresses "how fast the superconducting state disappears in high field". Its data is of great interest; it is essentially what is measured in transport properties in high field (thermal conductivity, ultrasonic attenuation, ...). In particular it is proportional to the slope of the magnetization **M** in high field, which can be written from a generalization of the Abrikosov result[8]

$$\frac{|\Delta|^2}{H_M - H} \alpha - 4\pi \left(\frac{dM}{dH}\right)_{H_M} = \frac{1}{\beta(\kappa_2^2(T) - J_2)}$$

(19)

1)

$$\beta = \frac{< |\Delta|^4 >}{< |\Delta^2| >^2}$$

gives a spatial average of the pair potential.

2) -J_2 is a measure of the strength of the screening currents below H_M (see a)). (It is obtained by an integral over j_s^2).

3) -$\kappa_2(T)$ is a parameter function of temperature whose normalization is such that it is equal to the G.L. parameter at T_c. It includes the effects of the spatial derivatives of Δ.

   $\kappa_2(T)$ increases when T decreases[7] for the vortex structure and in the case of the surface superconductivity (in the two cases the variation of $\Delta(\mathbf{r})$ can be taken as a gaussian). However for thin films with $d < \xi$ (T), $|\Delta|$ is practically independent of position. $\kappa_2(T)$ decreases with T as the parameter originally calculated by Maki.[3] $J_2 = 0$ when the effect of screening currents is negligible. (d is small with respect to the penetration depth λ (T)). Moreover $\beta = 1$.

III. TUNNELING IN HIGH FIELD

   We have studied these different behaviours by tunneling experiments on films. In the limit of high fields, the tunneling density of states of "dirty" superconductors is given by[2]

$$\frac{N(E) - N(0)}{N(0)} = \left(\frac{\Delta}{\epsilon_0(H)}\right)^2 f\left(\frac{E}{\epsilon_0(H)}\right) \tag{20}$$

where N(0) is the density of states in the normal state. The range of validity of this expansion is given by $\Delta \ll \epsilon_0(H)$ where Δ represents the strength of the superconducting perturbation.

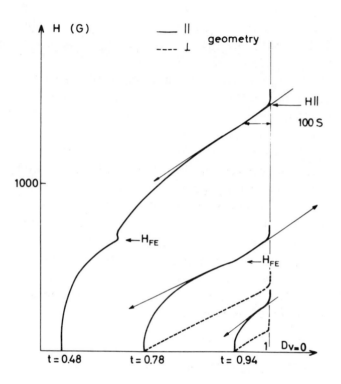

Fig. 2. Variation of the normalized initial slope of the tunneling characteristics with field. The high-field part of the t $(=T/T_c)$ = 0.48 curve shows typical determinations of the slope S on a 100-G interval and of the upper critical field (H_{11}). The parallel-field curve at t = 0.9 does not show the break which we associate at lower temperatures with the first entry of vortices in the film (H_{FE}). The structure at the break is usually more pronounced when $H_{FE} < H_{c2}$ (curve t = 0.48).

We will not discuss here the gapless shape[4] of the density of states given by the term $f(E/\epsilon_0(H))$. In the high field limit where $\epsilon_0(H)$ is given by (16) it is independent of the mechanism of field penetration and of the value of field.

All the information on these factors is included in Δ. It is possible to measure Δ from the variation of the initial slope of the tunneling characteristics with field:

$$\frac{|\Delta|^2}{H_M - H} \quad \text{is proportional to} \quad \frac{1 - D_{v=0}(H)}{H_M - H}$$

where

$$D(v) = \frac{dI}{dv} \Big/ \left(\frac{I}{v}\right)_N$$

(The normal state is given by $D(v) = 1$).

The figure (2) gives the typical result of the initial slope variation obtained on a thick InBi film at different temperatures

--When $T \to T_{c_S}$, the film is thin $(d/\xi(T) \to \infty)$.

—Below a certain temperature always given by $d/\xi(T) = 1.8$ one observes a break in this curve. The break becomes more pronounced at lower temperatures. The value H_{FE} of this field corresponds to the first penetration of vortices in the film. Qualitatively, when $T \to T_{C_S}$, the core of a vortex $\xi(T)$ is larger than d and the vortices cannot fit into the film. The penetration is possible at lower temperatures.

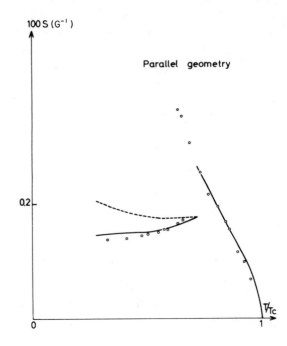

Fig. 3. Temperature variation of the high-parallel-field slope for an intermediate-thickness film showing the same behavior as in Fig. 2. The jump in slope is associated with the first occurrence of flux entry. The theoretical curve was fitted at the maximum value s = 0.26 and gives the right magnitude of the jump. Dashed line is the corresponding calculated curve in the dirty limit.

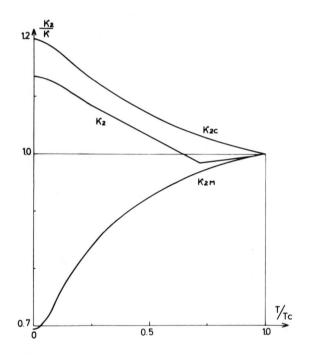

Fig. 4. The limiting form for κ_{2M} and κ_{2c} and that for the film of Fig. 3 as a function of T/T_c in the dirty limit.

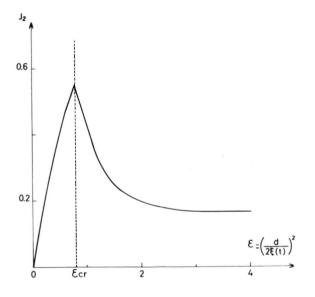

Fig. 5. J_2 shows the strength of screening currents. It goes to zero with ϵ; screening currents become negligible for thin films. It also decreases when the two sheaths of the surface state become farther apart. It is at a maximum with almost the value for the Abrikosov bulk type-II case at the point where the film can just accommodate vortices at H_M.

-- Finally at low temperatures, if the film is
thick enough, the solution will be similar to the
de Gennes-Saint James solution for surface
superconductivity.

The figure (3) shows the slope of $D_{V=0}(H)$ at H_M
as a function of temperature. There is a change of
slope by a factor $2/3$ at the temperature corresponding to the first entry of vortices.

These results are compared with a calculation[8]
based on the Abrikosov method and using the shape of
the solution of $\Delta(r)$ of the linearized G.L. equation
which is known for all values of $d/\xi_{(T)}$. We will
discuss the terms of this agreement.

a)   In a thin film, Δ is constant in the film and $\beta = 1$.
However as soon as $d/\xi_{(T)} > 1,8$ it was shown by
Saint James that this solution becomes unstable with
respect to the two dimensional solutions (see Tinkham,
same conference)

$$\Delta(r) = f(x) e^{iky} + if(-\kappa) e^{-iky} \qquad (21)$$

obtained by adding two sheaths centred on the faces
of the film. The film is limited by $x = \pm d/2$, and z is
the field direction. The choice of the phase difference
between the two terms is arbitrary.

$$|\Delta|^2 = f^2(x) + f^2(-x) + 2f(x)f(-\kappa)\sin 2ky \qquad (22)$$

In particular $|\Delta|^2$ vanishes at the centres of an array
of vortices at the values $2ky = -\pi/2 + 2n\pi$, $x = 0$. The
occurrence of surface superconductivity is associated

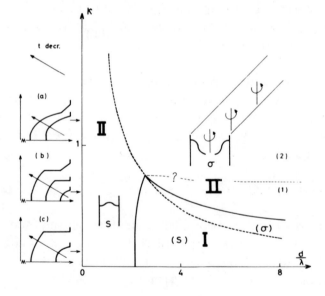

Fig. 6. (Left) Nucleation-field diagram for parallel fields. The dotted curve (d = 1.8 ξ or $\epsilon = \epsilon_{cr}$) separates a region to the left which cannot accommodate a vortex structure in high field (state S) and a complementary one which allows vortices (σ). The continuous curve which shows a cusp at $\epsilon = \epsilon_{cr}$ corresponds to the J_2 (ϵ) curve of Fig. 10. Above this curve the high-field transition is second order. Below it, it is first order : then (S) and (σ) refer to supercooling nucleation. This limiting curve is bounded on the left by the value $d/\lambda = \sqrt{5}$, which is the GL result. To the right it goes to $\kappa = 0.59$ ($H_{c3} = H_c$). The nearly horizontal line $\kappa = 0.7$ is guessed. It separates domains where the transition in the bulk will be first order (1) and second order (2) in lower fields. We give sets of $D_{V=0}$ (H) curves for three values of κ. (a) gives the same description as Fig. 2. (b) shows successively obtained first-, second-, and first-order transitions (c) is the usual set of curves for pure material (In).

with that of vortices in the thickness of the film.

$$\beta = \frac{< |\Delta|^4 >}{(< |\Delta|^2 >)^2} = \frac{3}{2}$$

as soon as $k \neq 0$ because of the average of the term $\sin^2 2ky$.

The observation of a change of slope of this value is a striking confirmation of the presence of the vortices in thick enough films.

b) The parameter κ_2 (fig. 4) indicates the importance of the spatial derivatives of Δ. Near T_{c_s} it decreases as the parameter calculated by Maki. Below the critical value given by $d/\ (T) = 1.8$, Δ varies much in the thickness of the film and κ_2 increases as the parameter for the vortex structure.

c) J_2 (fig. 5) has a maximum for the critical value. The value of the maximum corresponds nearly to that for the fluxoid structure in the bulk ($J_2 = 0.5$). This is reasonable as, for this value, the cores of the vortices just fit in the thickness of the film. For large d, J_2 goes to 0.15 for the de Gennes-Saint James surface superconductivity.

d) This last curve gives a way to construct a diagram for nucleation fields, if one replaces the ordinate J_2 by κ_2^2. For points below the curve the high field transition is first order because it is not thermodynamically possible to have a negative slope in (19). For larger values it will be second order if the nucleation field H_M is the upper critical field.

The fig. (6) represents the same diagram in co-ordinates κ, $d/\lambda(T)$ in the limit $T \to T_{cs}$ where $\kappa_2(T) \to \kappa = \lambda(T)/\xi(T)$. For large thicknesses the curve corresponds nearly to the condition $H_c = H_{c3}$*. For a small d and for $\kappa \to 0$ one gets the G.L. result for the change 1st to 2nd order transition, $d = \sqrt{5}\lambda(T)$.

We add the branch of hyperbola $d = 1.8\,\xi(T)$. To its right the nucleation field will be of de Gennes-Saint James type. To the left it will correspond to the symmetrical G.L. solution. Below the curve for the 1st-2nd order transition, the nucleation field corresponds to the supercooling field discussed previously by Burger.

A similar description can be performed for films in a perpendicular geometry.[8,9] In this case demagnetizing effects are important and have to be included in the definition of dM/dH as mentioned by Cape and Zimmermann.[10]

B. PROXIMITY EFFECTS

When a normal metal N is deposited on top of a superconductor S and if the electrical contact between the two is good, the two metals influence each other:

--In S the superconducting properties are

*In fact the condition $H_{c3} = 1.69\,\kappa_1\,\sqrt{2}\,H_c > H_c$ or $\kappa_1 > 1/1.69\sqrt{2}$ is met at lower temperatures than $\kappa_2^2 - 0.15 > 0$, as could be seen from the temperature dependence of the two κ parameters, and the condition $H_c = H_{c3}$ is a stronger requirement. However the difference between these two conditions is small and we will neglect it.

attenuated: there is a decrease of the critical
temperature and of the critical fields.

--In N there is an induced superconductivity
observable by the existence of persisting currents, the possibility of Meissner effect and by
nonlinear tunneling characteristics on N.

These phenomena are the "proximity effects"
(we will write P.E.). They are related to the
"leakage" of Cooper pairs from S to N. S is the producing "reservoir" and N is the unfavourable re-
ceiving one.

The thickness of the leakage region K^{-1} is typically 10^2 to 10^3 Å. The P.E. is of relatively long
range.

This P.E. can be studied between bulk materials.
However it would be difficult to obtain the requisite
good electrical contact between the materials in the
absence of any oxide or absorbed surface layers.

The use of superimposed films is rather convenient for these studies. By an immediate succes-
sion of evaporations it is possible, in general, to
limit the presence of insulating impurities between
the films. (However in the case of the highly oxidiz-
able Al experiments by Van Gurp in a rather poor
vacuum (10^{-5} torr) have failed to show any proximity
effect with Pb films on top of Al).

Moreover the study of "size effects" with normal
and superconducting films of respective thicknesses
of the order of the leakage characteristic lengths of N
and of the coherence length of S (also 10^2 to 10^4 Å)
will give a very fine tool for the detailed study of the
P.E.

I. TECHNICAL ASPECT

Meissner[2] first measured supercurrents flowing between two superconducting wires separated by a thin Au film deposited on one wire. Then Smith et al[3] reported that the T_c of Ag-Pb superimposed films decreased with the thickness of the normal Ag film, d_N, the thickness of the superconductor, d_S, being kept constant. However Rose Innes and Serin[4] pointed out from their work on Au/Sn sandwiches that this effect might be due in part to the formation of inter-metallic compounds. The annealing of a given sandwich had a marked effect on T_c. (The prediction of the possible diffusion between films on the basis of bulk data is delicate. Usually diffusion is measured over much larger length;—surface diffusion and dif-fusion at the grain boundaries play a major role in the case of films.)

In order to avoid these effects two techniques have been used:

Choice of Materials

If the two materials have no mutual solubility, nor form intermetallic compounds, they can be evaporated at room temperature.[5]

The following couples have been used: Pb/Cu or Au, In/Zn, Pb/Sn (in this last system, the re-duced solubility of Sn in Pb does not affect the criti-cal properties of Pb much). . .

In these conditions the T_c of the sandwiches shows no ageing effect.

Condensation of films at low temperatures

Hauser et al[6] have used sandwiches in which the first film was prepared at room temperature to get large mean free paths whereas the second one was condensed at liquid N_2 temperature to reduce the diffusion. The sandwich was always kept at low temperatures. Previous experiments by Hilsch[7] had been done on Pb/Cu sandwiches studied as deposited at liquid He temperature.

For such films, the residual mean free path is small and given by the size of the small crystallites. The characteristic distances in N and S are thus small. In order to observe size effects one has to use very thin films where the thickness is not accurately known.

N/S boundary problem

When the mean free path in N and S is low the detailed behaviour of the scattering of electrons at the interface is not important. In pure materials however a detailed description of the boundary properties is needed and influence the P.E. In particular they affect the nature of resonant structures (Tomasch effect)[8] due to the interference in one film of the quasiparticle states. We will not discuss here this resonance aspect.

II. THEORETICAL DESCRIPTION

1) Thin Films

The first and simplest case is that discussed by

Cooper[9] of thin N and S films. An electron spends part of its time in N and part in S. Due to the different densities of states in N and S (N_N, N_S) the normalized times spent can be taken as $N_N d_N$ and $N_S d_S$, and the average interaction potential

$$(V)_{av} = \frac{N_N d_N V_N + N_S d_S V_S}{N_N d_N + N_S d_S} \tag{1}$$

The critical temperature is given by the usual BCS expression, $T_c \propto \exp(-1/NV))$.[10] However experiments in this limit are limited because of the difficulty of obtaining very thin films of well defined thickness. Also, as pointed out by Bassewitz and Minnigerode some films (Cu) deposited at low temperature have properties different from the bulk (density, resistivity).

2)   De Gennes-Werthamer Solution for Dirty Materials

In the subcritical regime ($T \lesssim T_c$) $\Delta(\mathbf{r})$ is small and can be obtained from an expansion of the self consistent equation[11]

$$\Delta(\kappa) = V(\kappa) \, kT \sum_\omega \int H_\omega (x, x') \, \Delta (x') \, dx',$$

$$\omega = (2n + 1) \pi \, kT \tag{2}$$

as for a single superconductor. The range of the kernel in S and N is given by

$$\xi_{N,S}(\omega) = \sqrt{\frac{\hbar D_{N,S}}{2\,|\omega|}} \tag{3}$$

It is also possible to get from the self consistent equation the boundary conditions obeyed by the pair potential:

$$\left(\frac{\Delta}{NV}\right) \qquad \text{continuous} \tag{4}$$

$$D\frac{d}{dx}\left(\frac{\Delta}{V}\right) \qquad \text{continuous} \tag{5}$$

--When $V_N = 0$, $\Delta_N(x) = 0$ but $F(x) = \Delta/V$ has a finite tail in N due to the contributions of the pair amplitude in S. Keeping only the largest range solution

$$\xi_N = \sqrt{\frac{\hbar D_N}{2\pi\,kT}} \tag{6}$$

one gets

$$F_N(x) = F_N(0)\,e^{-kx} \tag{7}$$

with the leakage length $K^{-1} = \xi_N$.
The approximation does not apply well to thin films where all contributions to the kernel have to be considered.
--If $V_N > 0$, N is a superconductor at a temperature $T > T_{cN}$. When $T \to T_{cN}$ the characteristic length for variation of Δ_N diverges (Fluctuations at T_{cN} are critical).

We have shown in A a time dependent equation for a dirty superconductor below T_{cs}. In the same way we consider an infinite dirty N material at $T > T_{cN}$. We impose $\Delta_N \neq 0$ at $t = 0$. Δ will decay exponentially with time

$$\frac{\partial \Delta}{\partial t} = - \frac{\Delta}{\tau_N(t)} \tag{8}$$

If Δ is spatially varying and in the presence of a field, we have to add up a term expressing the diffusion of pairs and gauge covariance

$$\frac{\partial \Delta}{\partial t} = - \frac{\Delta}{\tau_N(t)} + D\left(\nabla - \frac{2ie}{\hbar c}\, \mathbf{A}\right)^2 \Delta. \tag{9}$$

For $T > T_{cN}$ $\tau_N(t)$ is given (see first part) by

$$\log \frac{T_{cN}}{T} = \Psi\left(\frac{1}{2} - \frac{\hbar}{4\pi\, kT\, \tau_N}\right) - \Psi\left(\frac{1}{2}\right) \tag{10}$$

The resulting equilibrium G.L. equation is given by putting $\partial \Delta/\partial t = 0$ in (9). For $H = 0$, $\Delta_N(x)$ decays exponentially. The leakage length is obtained from (9):

$$K^{-1} = \sqrt{D\, \tau_N(t)} \tag{11}$$

From (6), (10) and (11) one gets

$$\log \frac{T_{cN}}{T} = \Psi\left(\frac{1}{2} - K^2\, \xi_N^2\right) - \Psi\left(\frac{1}{2}\right) \tag{12}$$

This equation for K^{-1} has several roots. Werthamer has proposed to keep the smallest one, corresponding to the fastest decay of Δ in (7). The range of validity of this approximation is not well known. In the case of infinite thickness and with $V_N = 0$ it corresponds to an error of 10%. [12] The result (12) can be generalized at all temperatures $T \lesssim T_{CN}$ (For $T < T_{CN}$, $K^{-1} \to i\xi$ (T)).

Films of Finite Thicknesses (Fig. 1.)

The solution

$$\Delta_N(x) = \Delta(-d_N) \text{ ch } K(x + d_N) \tag{13}$$

obeys the boundary condition $\partial\Delta/\partial x = 0$ at the free surface of N and is the solution of the linearized G.L. equation in N at T_c. In the same way, the solution in S is

$$\Delta_S(x) = \Delta(d_S) \cos \frac{x - d_S}{\xi} . \tag{14}$$

From the conditions (4), (5) at x = 0 one gets

$$\frac{1}{\xi} \text{ tg } \frac{d_S}{\xi} = \frac{N_N D_N}{N_S D_S} K \text{ th } K d_n \tag{15}$$

It is an implicit equation in T by the terms ξ and K and has a single solution at T_c ($T_{cN} < T_c < T_{cS}$). The experiments give T_c, T_{cS}, d_n, d_S and the normal state conductivities; it is possible to predict a value of T_{cN} even when it is too small to be measured directly.

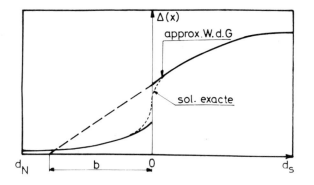

Fig. 1. Variation of the pair potential in a
Normal Superconductor sandwich in the
Werthamer de Gennes approximation.

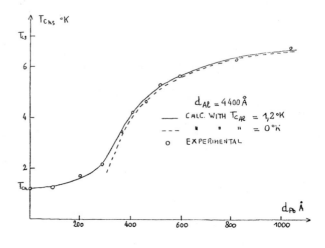

Fig. 2. T_c measurements of Pb/Al sandwiches. The difference between the curves calculated for the actual value of the interaction potential in N and with $V_N = 0$ is appreciable only close to $T_{cN} = 1.2$ K.

Results Pb/Al are given in fig. (2). The experiments
fit well with this model. However, in order to see a
marked difference between different values of V_N,
experiments at $T \sim T_{cN}$ are needed. This reduces
very much the interest or the accuracy of these determinations of T_{cN}.

When S is very thick, all effects in N can be incorporated in a single parameter, the <u>extrapolation
length</u> b defined by:

$$\frac{\partial \Delta_S}{\partial x}\bigg|_{x=0} = \frac{\Delta_S(0)}{b} \tag{16}$$

b measures the unfavourable influence of N on the
superconductivity in S.

If

$$b \ll \xi \quad \Delta \text{ vanishes at the interface}$$
$$\text{(strong P.E.)}$$
$$b \gg \xi \quad \Delta \text{ is constant near the interface}$$
$$\text{(no P.E.)}$$

By using the solution (13) the boundary condition
can be written

$$\frac{1}{\xi} \, tg \left(\frac{d_S}{\xi}\right) = \frac{1}{b} \tag{17}$$

If $d_S \gg b$ this equation gives

$$\frac{1}{\xi} = \frac{\pi}{2(d_S + b)} \, .$$

From the definition of ξ (T) (A, form. 3) the shift of
critical temperature

$$T_{cs} - T_c = \frac{\pi^2 \hbar^2}{8m A_0 (d_s + b)^2} \tag{18}$$

which varies as $1/d^2_s$ for large thicknesses.

In the Werthamer approach,

$$b = \frac{N_s D_s}{N_N D_N} \frac{\coth K d_N}{K} \tag{19}$$

is large for poor N conductors ($N_N D_N \ll N_S D_S$).
The proximity effect is weak. This can justify the
limit boundary condition $d/dx \, \Delta = 0$ at an interface
with an insulating material (see lectures by Tinkham).

Let us mention finally the expected effect between S and a magnetic material M:

As soon as a Cooper pair penetrates M one spin
direction is very favoured compared to the other.
The exchange energy Γ is very large (~ 1 e.V.) compared to the formation energy of a pair (0.001 eV)
and the pair is destroyed in M. $F(\mathbf{r}) = 0$ in M. If
the electrical contact is good enough, the Werthamer
boundary condition gives $\Delta(0^+) = 0$. Qualitatively
from the interaction energy Γ one gets that the uncertainty time for an electron to interact in M will be
$\sim \hbar/\Gamma$. It will have travelled a distance

$$b \sim \frac{\hbar}{M} V_F \sim 1 \, A^0 .$$

Experiments on Pb/Fe^6 agree with this result.
However because of the oxidation at the interface
the exact condition $b = 0$ is not always obtained.

The antiferromagnetic case (Mn, Cr) is not easy to treat.[13] Most of the effect is related to uncompensated spins acting as isolated magnetic impurities which are functions of the structural defects.

III. PROXIMITY EFFECT EXPERIMENTS

1) Tunneling Experiments at $T \lesssim T_c$

In a tunneling experiment between an homogeneous superconductor and a normal material the differential conductance is given by

$$\frac{dI}{dV} = \int_{-\infty}^{\infty} \frac{N_S(E)}{N(0)} \frac{\partial f(E - eV)}{\partial V} dE .$$

At low temperature $(\partial / \partial V) f$ goes to a δ-function and dI/dV measures directly the tunneling density of states.

Near T_{cs} the scale of the anomalies become small compared to $\Delta_0 = 1.75 \, kT_{cs}$ and the effect of the thermal broadening washes out most of the density of states information. It is in general difficult--and particularly in this limit—to calculate the density of states from the tunneling characteristics data. Even if the variation of $\Delta(x)$ is guessed, the calculation of the density of states, to be compared with the experiments, is difficult. When $T \sim T_c$, the deviation of the characteristics with respect to the normal state can be expressed as a power expansion.

$$1 - \left(\frac{dI}{dV}\right)\Big/\frac{I}{V} = |\Delta|^2 \, \phi \, (V)$$

where Δ is the value of the pair potential at the tunneling free surface and $\phi(V)$ depends on all the parameters of the 2 films.

This is analogous to the gapless behaviour of a single superconductor in field although there is no antisymmetric interaction. (The variation of $\Delta(x)$ is equivalent in the ∇ term to the effect of the field through the $(-i\hbar \nabla - 2l \, \mathbf{A}/c)$ term).[14] De Gennes and Mauro[15] have carried out a detailed analysis of the expression first obtained by Fulde and Maki[16] and shown that in general the proximity effect case is not strictly gapless as soon as the average of $|\Delta|^2$ in the film is $\neq 0$. However the effect of the thermal smearing is such that the difference is unobservable.

2) Tunneling Experiments from the S Side

The shape of the characteristics is not very different from that of a single film. The length explored in the tunneling experiment can be obtained by saying that the contribution at a depth x varies as $\Delta e^{-x/\xi}$ (20)

$$\text{with } \xi = \sqrt{\frac{\hbar D}{2\pi \, kT}} \qquad (20)^{5,\,15}$$

Δ_S does not vary much on this length and the situation is nearly the same as for a single superconductor. However the amplitude of Δ_S can be smaller than Δ_{S0} (in the absence of P.E.) when $T_c < T_{cs}$.

3) Tunneling from the N Side

When looking deeper in the film, the effect of the increase of Δ in (20) compensates the effect of the exponential. Even for large d_N, the value of the pair potential in S is important. $\phi(V)$ has to be calculated from the knowledge of Δ in N and S. We have obtained[17] a very good agreement between the residual density of states calculated without any adjustable parameter and tunneling experiments on the Zn side of Zn/**In** Bi sandwiches. $\Delta_N(-d_N)$ can be measured from the variation of the initial slope of the tunneling characteristics $|\Delta_N(-d_N)|^2 \alpha 1 - \phi(0)$. It varies with temperature as

$$\left(1 - \frac{T}{T_{c_S}}\right)^2$$

as can be seen in fig. (3). This result is different from from the BCS one where the initial slope varies more rapidly with T

$$(\Delta^2 \alpha \left(1 - \frac{T}{T_{c_S}}\right)).$$

To understand this result we consider the case $d_S \to \infty$. $\Delta_S(x)$ varies as th $(x - x_0)/\xi$. If we approximate the fast variation with a linear one

$$\Delta_S(0) = \Delta_S(\infty) \frac{b}{\xi} \alpha \left(1 - \frac{T}{T_{c_S}}\right)^{1/2} \left(1 - \frac{T}{T_{c_S}}\right)^{1/2}$$

$$= 1 - \frac{T}{T_{c_S}}.$$

Far from T_{cN}, $\Delta_N(d_N)$ is just proportional to $\Delta_S(0)$.
This behaviour, drastically different from a B.C.S. one, shows in particular that the induced

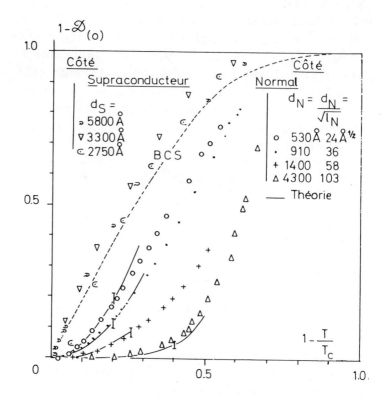

Fig. 3. Temperature variation of the initial slope of the tunneling characteristics taken on the two sides of Zn/In̲ Bi sandwiches. On the superconducting side, the slope varies nearly as in the BCS case (near T_c Δ^2 α $1 - D(0)$ α $T_c - T$). It is very different on the N side ($|\Delta|^2$ α $(T_{c_S} - T)^2$).

proximity in N is not just an effect related to diffusion of S, or to a porous N material.

The overall agreement has given a good justification of the de Gennes Werthamer model. One cannot use directly however the variation of Δ_N (-d_N) to get the profile of variation of Δ_N (x); $\Delta_N(0)$ depends on d_N.

4) Gapless Superconductivity by Proximity with a
. Magnetic Material

(See first lecture by P. Fulde).

5) Microwave Study

Another complementary way to study the P.E. is by microwave studies. The low lying excitations in N are those travelling parallel to the free surface. They should be detected more easily by a microwave experiment than by tunneling. Fisher and Klein[18] have analyzed their results on Cu/Pb sandwiches taking into account the variation of Δ with thickness and obtained a positive value | NV | for Cu.

6) Critical Current of an S/N/S Sandwich

The initial Meissner experiments have been developed recently by Clarke (preprint) who measured the very small transverse resistance of a thin Cu film ($d \sim 1000$ A^0) sandwiched between two films of Pb. He used a very sensitive Josephson effect detector able to measure 10^{-13} V. At low enough temperature a supercurrent can flow through N. The critical current $I_c(T)$ for a typical sandwich shows two features;

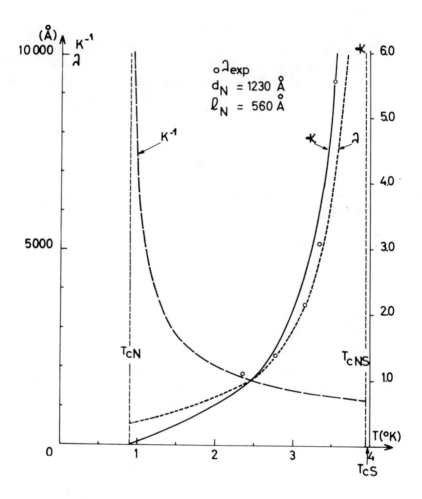

Fig. 5. Temperature dependence of the penetration depth λ (exp. and theory), the leakage length K^{-1}, and the effective G.L. parameter at the Zn free surface of Zn/**In** Bi sandwich. Actually K should go to the G.L. value of Zn at T_{cN}.

these are: $T_c < T_{cpb}$ and for $T < T_c$, $I_c(T)$ varies less rapidly than for an isolated superconductor.

There is an analogy between such a sandwich and a Josephson junction S/I/S where the pair current can be thought to be due to the proximity induced in $I(F_I(x) \neq 0)$. The super current is proportional to Δ^2 and varies as $1 - (T/T_{cs})$ in the S/I/S case. In the S/N/S case, Δ_s decreases near the interface. We have calculated in III 2 the temperature dependence of

$$\Delta_s(0) \; \alpha \; \left(1 - \frac{T}{T_{c_s}} \right)$$

at the S/N interface. The critical current is expected to vary as $1 - (T/T_{c_s})^2$ as is observed by Clarke. These results can be compared to those of the initial slope of the tunneling characteristics which measure the lowering of the pair potential in N.

IV. MAGNETIC FIELD BEHAVIOUR

1) Zero Field Case: Meissner Effect

Let us recall that in general the penetration depth $\lambda(x) \; \alpha \; 1/\Delta(x)$; the screening of the field becomes weaker, λ increase when the pair potential decreases. In the P.E. case λ is a function of position that can be obtained from dynamic susceptibility data.[19]

The penetration of field is characterized by a parameter, corresponding to the usual G.L. parameter, a function of position:

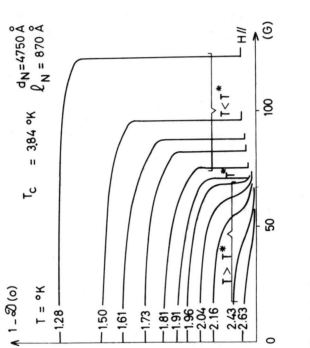

Fig. 6. Variation of the initial slope of a tunneling characteristic on the N side of a Zn/**In** Bi 2% sandwich taken as a function of a field parallel to the free surfaces. At low temperatures, the transition at the breakdown field H_b is first order.

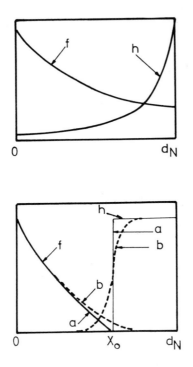

Fig. 7. At $T < T^*$, 2 modes of penetration of the field are possible: --upper part: $\Delta(-d_N)$, (f), is large enough and the field (h in reduced units) is screened near the free N surface. --lower part: Δ is practically zero from $|x_0|$ to $|d_N|$. The field penetrates freely up to x_0.

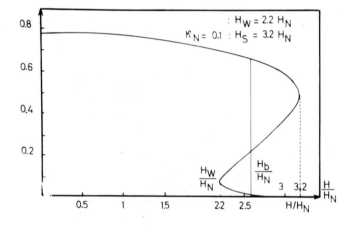

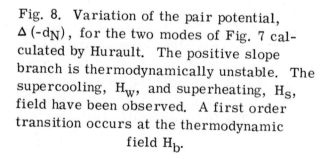

Fig. 8. Variation of the pair potential,
$\Delta(-d_N)$, for the two modes of Fig. 7 calculated by Hurault. The positive slope
branch is thermodynamically unstable. The
supercooling, H_W, and superheating, H_S,
field have been observed. A first order
transition occurs at the thermodynamic
field H_b.

$$K_N(x) = \frac{\lambda(x)}{K^{-1}} \cdot K_N(x)$$

is minimum near the interface where Δ is large and screening effects important. It increases near the free surface of N. We are mainly concerned with its value K_N at the free surface of N where measurements are done. When $V_N > 0$, K_N goes from infinity at T_c ($\lambda \to \infty$) to zero at T_{cN} ($K^{-1} \to \infty$) (fig. 5). A more detailed study gives the reasonable result that K_N goes to the value of the G.L. parameter of N at T_{cN}. The difference is not important in general: if T_{cN} is small, the B.C.S. coherence length is large and K_N will be small.

From the variation of K_N we predict two regimes:

1) $K_N(-d_N) > 1$. The magnetic field penetrates freely. This case was met in experiments by Fanelli and Meissner[20] who found that Au films backed by Sn do not screen the field down to $1\,°K$.

2) $K_N(-d_N) < 1$ (Low temperature case). When $T \searrow$, $\Delta_N \nearrow$, $\lambda \searrow$ and K^{-1} becomes large near T_{cN}. Appreciable screening currents have been observed in Zn backed by In at temperatures as high as $3\,T_{cN}$.[21] No such effect has been observed in Cu backed by Pb down to $1\,°K$, indicating that if a superconductor, Cu has a rather low T_c.

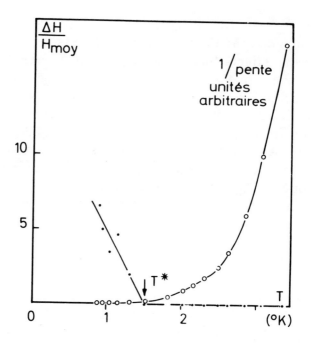

Fig. 9. T* can be measured from the
hysteresis in D (u) in increasing or decreasing field ($\Delta H = H_S - H_W$) when the
transition is first order. The determination
agrees with that based on the measurements
of the slope of Fig. 6 near H_b.

2) Magnetic Field Behaviour in the Normal Side

The Meissner effect in N can be detected from the change in penetration depth with a magnetic field parallel to the surfaces or from that of Δ_N. The variation of the pair potential Δ ($-d_N$) is measured by the initial slope of the characteristics on the Zn side of Zn/InBi sandwiches at different temperature in fig. (6). At high temperature, Δ ($-d_N$) decreases continuously. Below a certain temperature T^*, there is a first order transition at a field H_b towards a state where Δ ($-d_N$) is essentially zero. Microwave experiments on similar sandwiches[18] show an increase of absorption above H_b due to the normal electrons near the free surface in N.

Qualitatively the two behaviours can be thought of as a single superconductor with a G.L. parameter K_N.

1) For $T < T^*$, K_N is small. Two modes of penetration are possible. In the first one Δ ($-d_N$) is large enough and there is an appreciable screening of the field (fig. 7a). In the second one, the field has penetrated up to a thickness x_0; $\Delta(x)$ is small for $|x| > x_0$ (fig. 7b). The variation of Δ ($-d_N$) is given for the two modes in fig. (8). The positive slope branch is one where the flux decreases when H increases and is unstable thermodynamically. H_b is determined as in a usual Clapeyron diagram. H_s and H_w are superheating and supercooling fields as discussed by Burger for a single 1st kind superconductor (same conference).

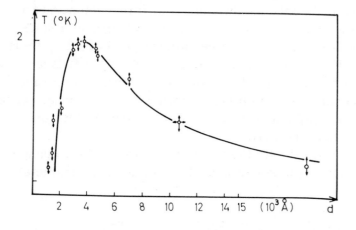

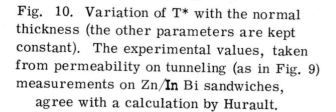

Fig. 10. Variation of T* with the normal thickness (the other parameters are kept constant). The experimental values, taken from permeability on tunneling (as in Fig. 9) measurements on Zn/In Bi sandwiches, agree with a calculation by Hurault.

2) For $T > T,*$ there is a single mode of penetration. $\Delta(-d_N)$ varies continuously with H.

The measurement of the hysteresis of the tunneling characteristics in increasing and decreasing field gives a way to get T*. An example of such measurement is given in fig. 9.
The variation of T* with d_N for a given couple of materials has been calculated by Hurault[12] and is in good agreement with actual results on In Bi/Zn sandwiches (fig. 10). The curve has a maximum for $d_N \sim K^{-1}$

—When d_N becomes larger, $K_N(-d_N)$ increases and the screening of field at a given temperature is weaker. T* decreases.
—When d_N becomes smaller than K^{-1}, the energy required for the distortion of Δ_N in a distance d_N is large. The presence of a wall in the width of N is unfavourable. T* decreases with d_N.

ACKNOWLEDGMENTS

I want to emphasize that these talks are the result of the work of all the Orsay group on Superconductivity.

REFERENCES PART A

1. For a general presentation of the G.L. equations, see de Gennes P.G. Superconductivity of metals and Alloys New York, Benjamin 1966.

2. de Gennes, P. G.: Phys. Kond. Mat. 3, 79 (1964).

3. Maki, K.: Physics 1, 21 (1964).

4. Guyon, E.: Adv. in Phys. 15, 417 (1966).

5. Suhl, H.: Bull. Am. Phys. Soc. 6, 119 (1961).

6. Abrahams, E. and T. Tsuneto: Phys. Rev. 152, 416 (1966).

7. Caroli, C., M. Cyrot and P. G. de Gennes: Sol. St. Comm. 4, 17 (1966).

8. Guyon, E., F. Meunier and R. S. Thompson: Phys. Rev. 156, 452 (1967).

9. Maki, K. Ann. in Phys. 34, 363 (1965).

10. Cape, J. A. and J. M. Zimmerman: Phys. Rev. 153, 416 (1967).

REFERENCES PART B

1. Van Gurp, C. J.: Phys. Lett. 5, 303 (1963).

2. Meissner, H.: Phys. Rev. 117, 672 (1960).

3. Smith, P. H., S. Shapiro, J. L. Miles and J. Nichol: Phys. Rev. Lett. 6, 686 (1961).

4. Rose Innes, A. C. and B. Serin: Phys. Rev. Lett. 7, 278 (1961).

5. See A. Martinet, Chap. II These, Orsay (1966).

6. Hauser, J. J., H. C. Theurer and N. R. Werthamer: Phys. Rev. 142, 118 (1966).

7. Hilsch, P. and R. Hilsch: Zeit. Phys. 138, 109 (1954).

8. See Tomasch, W. Proceedings of the Risö conference on Electrontunneling (1967) to be published.

9. Cooper, L. N.: Phys. Rev. Lett. 6, 698 (1961).

10. T_{cs} is the critical temperature of the isolated superconductor, T_c that of the sandwich. The films are limited by

11. de Gennes, P. G. and E. Guyon,: Phys. Lett. 3, 168 (1963).
    de Gennes, P. G.: Rev. Mod. Phys. 36, 225 (1964).

12. Hurault, J. P.: These, Orsay (1968).

13. de Gennes, P. G. and G. Deutscher: A Treatise on Superconductivity (Parks, R. D.) to be published.

14. Maki, K.: ibid.

15. de Gennes, P. G. and S. Mauro: Sol. St. Comm. 3, 381 (1965).

16. Fulde, P. and K. Maki: Phys. Rev. Lett. 15, 675 (1965).

17. Guyon, E., A. Martinet, S. Mauro and F. Meunier: Phys. Kond. Mat. 5, 123 (1966).

18. Fischer, G. and R. Klein: Phys. Kond. Mat. 7, 12 (1968).

19. Deutscher, G.: Jour. Phys. Chem. Sol. 28, 741 (1967).

20. Fanelli, R. and H. Meissner: Phys. Rev. 147, 227 (1967).

21. Orsay group on Superconductivity: Phys. Kond. Mat.

BEHAVIOUR OF TYPE II SUPERCONDUCTORS IN HIGH FIELDS

E. Saur

BEHAVIOUR OF TYPE II SUPERCONDUCTORS
IN HIGH FIELDS

E. Saur
Institute of Applied Physics
University of Giessen
Giessen, W. Germany

I. EXPERIMENTAL RESULTS

In some preliminary papers[1] we have reported
on measurements carried out on some type II superconductors up to very high fields. In the meantime
more measurements have been done, and the results
on NbN have been published in detail.[2] The details on
critical data of β-W compounds are to be published.[3,4]
The critical field curves for some compounds are
given in Fig. 1. The critical fields up to 150 kOe
have been measured directly, but the higher critical
fields at 4.2 °K for the β-W compounds have been
determined by extrapolation of quenching curves to
currents as low as 5 mA. The quenching curves of
V_3Si and V_3Ga with various conditions of preparation
are given as examples in Fig. 2 and 3, respectively.
The experimental values of the upper critical fields
$H_{c2}(4.2)$ at 4.2 °K and the extrapolated values of the
upper critical fields $H_{c2}(0)$ at zero temperature are

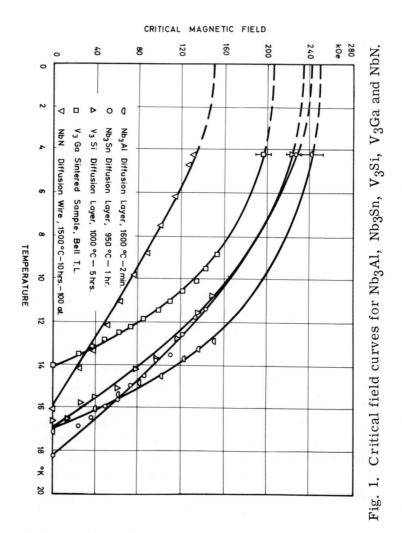

Fig. 1. Critical field curves for Nb$_3$Al, Nb$_3$Sn, V$_3$Si, V$_3$Ga and NbN.

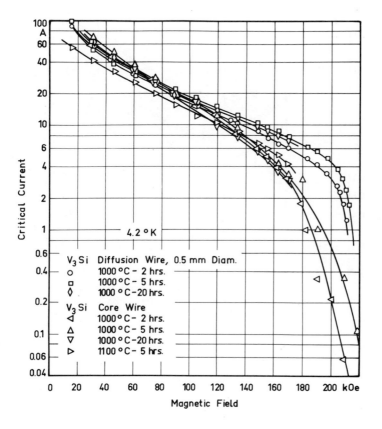

Fig. 2. Quenching curves for different
samples of V₃Si.

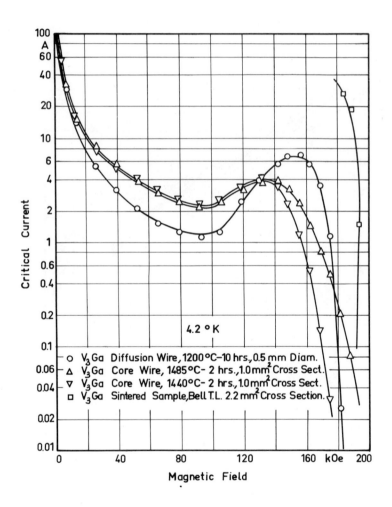

Fig. 3. Quenching curves for different
samples of V₃Ga.

TABLE 1: Upper Critical Field Values at 4.2 °K and Zero Temperature

	Nb_3Al	Nb_3Sn	V_3Si	V_3Ga	NbN	
$H_{c2}(4.2)$	242	225	220	196	132	kOe
$H_{c2}(0)$	252	245	235	208	153	kOe

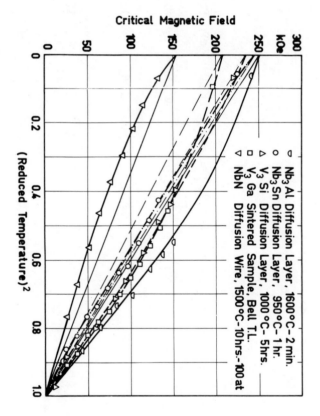

Fig. 4. Critical fields as a function of the
square of reduced temperature.

listed in Table 1. All measurements have been done at the MIT Francis Bitter National Magnet Laboratory Cambridge, Mass., U.S.A., using Bitter type solenoids for the generation of the high fields.

II. THE SHAPE OF THE CRITICAL FIELD CURVES

To check the critical field curves on parabolic shape the critical field values have to be plotted versus T^2 or $t^2 = (T/T_c)^2$. For the values given in Fig. 1 this has been done in Fig. 4. The deviation from the parabolic shape is clearly to be seen. Only the critical field values for Nb_3Sn are represented nearly by a straight line. The real shape of the critical field curves can be obtained from a formula given by Werthamer et al.[5] taking into account Pauli-paramagnetism and spin-orbit scattering in the super-conductor. By using the experimental values of Maki-parameters α and fitting the curves by selected values of λ_{so}, which measures the spin-orbit effect, the theoretical curves for the β-W compounds in Fig. 5 have been drawn. The matching of experimental values and theoretical curves is fairly good and is a method of determining λ_{so}. For more details compare the paper of Hechler et al.[4]

III. COMPARISON OF EXPERIMENTAL RESULTS WITH RECENT THEORY

In a recent theory Helfand and Werthamer[6] give an equation for the reduced initial slope

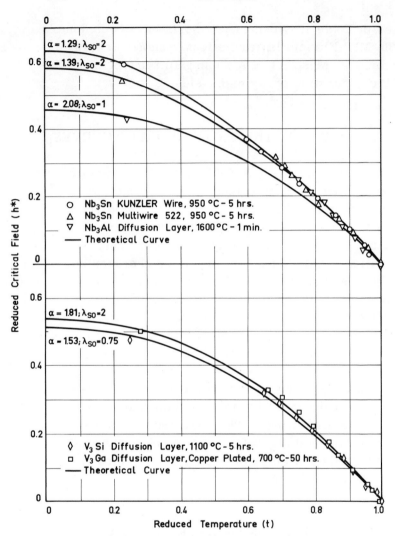

Fig. 5. Reduced critical field curves for some β-W compounds, experimental and theoretical.

$$- \left(\frac{dh}{dt}\right)_{t=1}$$

of the critical field curve as a function of the reduced mean number of collisions ρ, which is defined by:

$$\rho = 8.85 \cdot 10^3 \cdot \gamma^{1/2} \cdot \rho_n / \kappa_0$$

where γ is the electron specific heat coefficient in $erg/cm^3 (°K)^2$, ρ_n the normal state resistivity just above T_c in Ω cm, and κ_0 the Ginzburg-Landau parameter in the pure limit. The reduced slope of the upper critical field curves at T_c or $t = 1$ may be calculated from experimental data by the formula:[7]

$$-\left(\frac{dh}{dt}\right)_{t=1} = \frac{0.5807}{\kappa_0} \cdot \frac{T_c}{H_c(0)} \cdot \left(-\frac{dH_{c2}}{dT}\right)_{T=T_c}$$

where $H_c(0)$ is the thermodynamical critical field at zero temperature:

$$H_c(0) = 2.24 \cdot \gamma^{1/2} \cdot T_c$$

and

$$\left(-\frac{dH_{c2}}{dT}\right)_{T=T_c}$$

the initial slope of the critical field curves, which may be taken from Fig. 1. In Fig. 5 the experimental data of the reduced initial slope

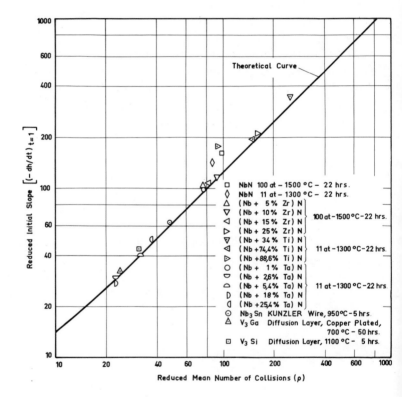

Fig. 6. Reduced initial slopes of critical
field curves versus reduced mean number
of collisions.

$$\left(-\frac{dh}{dt}\right)_{t=1}$$

for a variety of type II superconductors are plotted versus ρ. They fit well the theoretical curve after Helfand and Werthamer,[6] which is also shown. Fietz and Webb[7] have presented results for other type II superconductors in the range of ρ from 0.001 to 20. So our results give a continuation up to $\rho = 300$. More details will be given in the paper by Hechler et al.[4] We wish to thank the Deutsche Forschungsgemeinschaft, the Stiftung Volkswagenwerk and the Fraunhofer-Gesellschaft for financial support.

REFERENCES

1. Saur, E. and H. Wizgall: Les Champs Magnétiques Intenses, Colloque International, Grenoble 1966, p. 223

   Saur, E. and H. Wizgall: Proc. 10th Intern. Conf. Low Temp. Phys. Moscow 1966, p.

   Saur, E. and H. Wizgall: Proc. ICEC 1, Tokyo and Kyoto 1967, p. 156.

2. Hechler, K., E. Saur and H. Wizgall: Z. Physik 205, 400 (1967).

3. Otto, G., E. Saur and H. Wizgall: Z. Physik (in preparation).

4. Hechler, K., G. Horn, G. Otto and E. Saur: Z. Physik (in preparation).

5. Wethamer, N. R., E. Helfand and P. C. Hohenberg: Phys. Rev. 147, 295 (1966).

6. Helfand, E. and N. R. Werthamer: Phys. Rev. 147, 288 (1966).

7. Fietz, W. A. and W. W. Webb: Phys. Rev. 161, 423 (1967).

SUPERCONDUCTIVITY
IN THE TRANSITION METALS:
PHONONS AND SPIN FLUCTUATIONS

M. Anthony Jensen

SUPERCONDUCTIVITY
IN THE TRANSITION METALS:
PHONONS AND SPIN FLUCTUATIONS

M. Anthony Jensen
University of Pennsylvania, Philadelphia

ABSTRACT

We describe the existing experimental and theoretical understanding of the many-body effects in transition metals which are caused by the ion-density fluctuations (phonons) and electron spin-density fluctuations (paramagnons).

I. INTRODUCTION

Most of the work reported at this summer institute is concerned with a few elements, e.g., Pb has been extensively studied. We take a different point of view here and look at the behavior of superconductivity in a whole series of metals – in particular, the transition metals. We are not primarily interested in the properties in the superconducting state since they are explained rather well by the modified BCS theory parameterized by the transition temperature T_c.

Rather, we want to study the behavior of T_c itself. In particular we would like to know if the pairing is always caused by the electron-phonon interaction or if other mechanisms are also responsible for the pairing. Also, we want to determine if repulsive mechanisms other than the static coulomb repulsion are important in suppressing the pairing. We should keep in mind during these lectures that we are generally at a severe handicap in studying these metals because their bond structure and other "normal state" properties are not yet well understood. Nevertheless, some general progress is possible if we keep from getting lost in the details and seek a more qualitative understanding. Such an understanding is the objective of these lectures.

First of all to gain some perspective let us look at the variation of superconductivity in the transition series as a whole. In Fig. 1, we plot the behavior of T_c along the 3d, 4d, and 5d series with Z the number of valence electrons/atom as the parameter.[1] The usefulness of such a point of view was first demonstrated by Matthias.[2] We see from this figure that the variation of T_c depends predominately on the parameter Z with very little dependence upon the row (3d, 4d or 5d until the d elements become magnetic; $Z \geq 6$). This is strong evidence for the applicability of a rigid band model. Also we see that there are two peaks in T_c at $Z = 5$, 7 and that the elements at the ends ($Z \sim 3$ and $Z \sim 10$) are not superconducting, with the exception of La. In terms of the rigid band systematics seen in this figure La is really an anomally and we will take some time later discussing it in detail. We should emphasize here that one can show in a large number of cases that the systematics represented by Fig. 1 is remarkably well followed. For example, if we mix

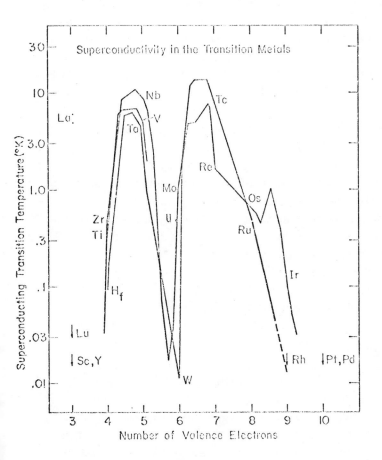

Fig. 1. The behavior of the superconducting transition temperature T_c among the transition metal elements and alloys. The parameter Z is the number of valence electrons per atom. For data in the figure and unless indicated in all the following figures see reference 1.

equal amounts of an element with Z = 4 and an element with Z = 6 you will find T_c very nearly that of a Z = 5 element, and so on.[1] Our purpose here is first to attempt to understand the systematics for the central transition metals $4 < Z < 8$ and then to understand the anomolous behavior of La(Z = 3). In all this we will be predominately concerned with the phonon interaction and the many-body effects it introduces in metals. Then we will turn our attention to the nearly-magnetic elements (Pt, Pd; Z = 10) and study the many-body effects present in these metals because of the spin density fluctuations (paramagnons). In these latter metals the superconductivity is strongly inhibited by the ferromagnetic spin correlations which lead to low frequency-long wavelength paramagnons.

The Bardeen-Cooper-Schrieffer[3] (BCS) theory of superconductivity in its original form gives a very simple expression for the superconducting transition temperature T_c (which we will discard later for a more sophisticated but rather similar one)

$$T_c \sim \langle \omega_c \rangle \, \exp[-1/N(0)V] \qquad (1)$$

where $\langle \omega_c \rangle$ is a cut off frequency for the attractive interactions (e.g., a phonon frequency) N(o) is the Fermi surface density of states and V is the net attractive coupling between electrons at the Fermi surface from (e.g.) phonon attraction and Coulomb repulsions. Initially it was speculated that V might be roughly constant at least among the transition metals,[4] and we will check this below.

First, let us see how N(o) varies along (with changing Z) the transition metals. In some schematic way we might expect transition metals to have two

bands (s and d), the former (s) almost plane wave
like and the latter (d) more nearly approximated by
tight binding. The density of states versus energy for
such a metal is shown schematically in Fig. 2. We
see that the density of states in the d-band is very
much larger than that in the s-band and hence the d-
band plays a dominate role in the thermodynamic properties. In reality there is a great deal of hybridization
between the two bands and one should really speak
only of Bloch electrons properly orthogonalized to
core states and having therefore a certain s-d like
character near the ions. We can more clearly see
that this is the case by looking at the band calculations
of Matthies[5] for the bcc phases of V, Cu and Fe. The
one-electron dispersion curves are shown in Fig. 3.
We see a large degree of hybridization. Also notice
that the flat E versus k curves indicate the very narrow bands associated with heavy (d-like) electrons.
The density of states is just (dE/dk) and so these flat
dispersion curves contribute regions of high density
of states as we showed in Fig. 2. Also notice that
the variation in the band structure among (with increasing Z) the three elements in Fig. 3 is rather
small. It is as though one just changed the position of
the Fermi level by pouring in more electrons. Thus
we have some support for the concept of a rigid band
in which one pours electrons; the parameter Z just
tells how full to fill the band and so if the band stays
rigid the metal's properties will be a function of the
single parameter Z. We will see later that in certain
cases when the atomic volume V_a is changing that the
bands also change and so Z is not the porper parameter (then we use Z/V_a = electron density) but for our
qualitative purpose here Z is sufficient.

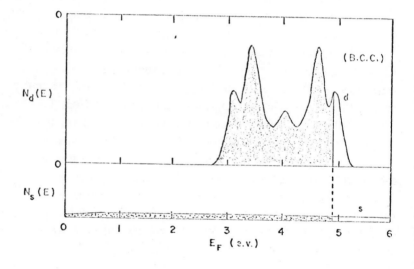

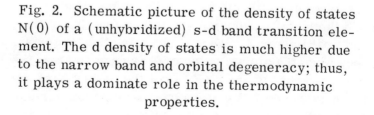

Fig. 2. Schematic picture of the density of states
N(0) of a (unhybridized) s-d band transition element. The d density of states is much higher due
to the narrow band and orbital degeneracy; thus,
it plays a dominate role in the thermodynamic
properties.

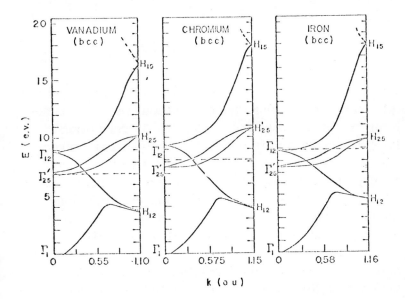

Fig. 3. The one-electron energy-momentum relations for the bcc phases of the elements V, Cr,
Fe as calculated by Matthies (see reference 5).
The s-d hybridization and rigid band behavior
with increasing Z are apparent. The flat E-k
curves are high density of states regions.

We can determine the density of states at the Fermi surface by measuring the electronic specific hear, γT. However, as we will discuss in more detail below the many body interactions affect the size of the specific heat which we measure. In particular, the phonons and paramagnons both cause γ to be enhanced from the one-electron value γ_0 by the mass enhancement factor m^*/m.

$$\gamma = \frac{m^*}{m} \gamma_0 = \frac{m^*}{m} \frac{\pi^2}{3} k_B^2 N(0) \tag{2}$$

where $N(o)$ is the density of states which one would obtain from a band structure calculation. As we will see later $m^*/m \lesssim 2$ for most metals but is very often larger than 1.5 and is therefore an important correction to γ. Thus, although the quantitative behavior of $N(0)$ is not directly obtained from specific heat measurements; nevertheless, we can qualitatively study the variation of $N(o)$ among the transition metals by looking at the behavior of γ. This is shown in figure 4 for both transition and non-transition metals. We see that the γ values for the transition metals are much larger than for the non-transition metals and that the variation with Z is very rapid, indicating a rapid variation of $N(\epsilon)$ with ϵ (or $N(0)$ with Z). These features agree with our expectations from the discussion above.

In order to determine the behavior of V in (1) we also need a phonon cutoff frequency (assuming for now that the electron-phonon interaction is the only attractive interaction). In general neutron scattering has been carried out only for a few elements among the transition metals. For example, in figure 5, we show the phonon dispersion curves for Nb and Mo (both bcc).

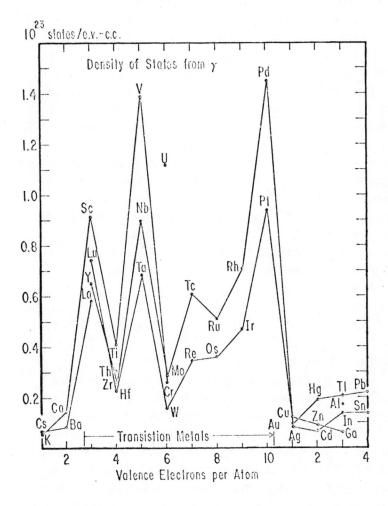

Fig. 4. Variation of the specific heat among the elements showing the very large values of γ (and hence $N(0)$) in the transition elements.

We indicate on the curves the frequency which corresponds to the phonon energy $k_B \theta_D$ (obtained for specific heat data) and we see that θ_D does give a qualitative measure of the cutoff of the phonon frequency spectrum. Thus we will use the measured values of θ for $\langle \omega_c \rangle$ in (1). We can see how θ_D varies along the transition metal series in Fig. 6. Perhaps the only systematics are dips at the magic numbers Z = 5, 7 and at Z=10. Also we note that the θ_D of La is anomalously low, falling with the Rare Earths and Activides rather than with the other 5d transition metals. We note that generally θ_D varies by only about a factor of two (300-600°K) among all the transition metals so its variation in (1) is not of qualitative significance since T_c is varying from below 10^{-2} °K to above 10°K. But we will find below that V in (1) is larger for a softer lattice which is characterized by a low θ_D value. This then is the significance of the θ_D dips at La, at Z $\sim$ 5, 7, and 10. (But T_c is not large at Z $\sim$ 10, indicating a repulsive contribution to the pairing interaction—Enough of giving away the plot.)

Let us return to our simple minded beginning. Now that we have a way of determining experimentally everything in (1) but V, we can calculate V and see how it varies. In particular, is it a constant among the transition metals? We plot the results of the calculation in Fig. 7 for all superconducting elements. We see that V is much larger in the non-transition metals (perhaps due to less screening) than in the transition metals. Although there does appear to be some systematic variation of V in the transition metals, it is certainly not even approximately a constant. But we know that the BCS theory is a weak-coupling theory and so we should bring our treatment of the interactions

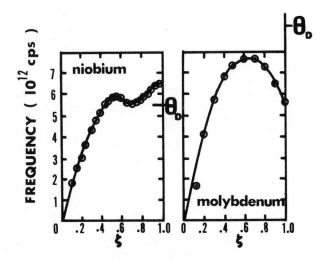

Fig. 5. The phonon energy-momentum dispersion relations for Nb(bcc) and Mo(bbc) the Debye frequency $(k_B \theta_D / \hbar)$ is indicated for each element by the horizontal bar.

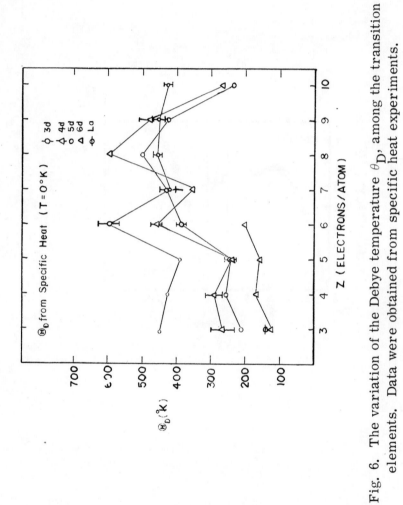

Fig. 6. The variation of the Debye temperature θ_D, among the transition elements. Data were obtained from specific heat experiments.

causing the superconductivity (and electron mass enhancement) up to date. Below we next describe schematically the strong coupling theory of superconductivity, in particular, as applied by McMillan[6] to transition metal superconductivity.

II. PHONONS AND STRONG COUPLING THEORY IN THE TRANSITION METALS

A. The Electron-Phonon Interaction

We write the transition temperature formula

$$T_c = \theta_D \exp[-1/G] \tag{3}$$

where in BCS weak coupling theory

$$G_{BCS} = N(0) V_{ph} - N(0) V_c = \lambda - \mu \tag{4}$$

defining the dimensionless parameters $\lambda \equiv N(o) V_{ph}$ and $\mu = N(o) V_c$ following Morel and Anderson.[7] λ and μ gauge the size of the phonon attraction and the Coulomb repulsion, respectively. As discussed in detail by Dr. Carbotte,[8] λ comes from the electron-displaced ion interaction. The coupling between an electron and the ion is written $g_{\mathbf{p'},\mathbf{p}}$ for an electron scattered from the initial state p to the final state $\mathbf{p'}$ with momentum $\mathbf{p'} - \mathbf{p} \equiv \mathbf{q}$ given to the lattice. The lattice displacement is expanded in terms of the normal modes of the lattice phonons and then we have

$$g_{\mathbf{p'},\mathbf{p}} = \left(\frac{\hbar}{2MN\,\omega_q}\right)^{1/2} I(\mathbf{p'},\mathbf{p}) \tag{5}$$

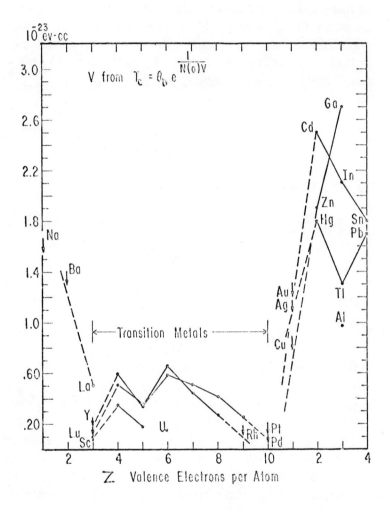

Fig. 7. The variation of the "BCS" net attractive interaction obtained from the BCS weak coupling formula using experimental T_c, θ, and γ data as discussed in the text.

where we drop the polarization index, $I(p', p)$ is an
electronic matrix element $(\mathbf{q} \cdot \epsilon \ (q) \ \langle p'|\omega|p\rangle$, see Dr.
Carbotte's lectures). The interaction of an electron
with the lattice vibrations is a many-body effect because it is sensitive to the presence of the other
electrons; they restrict the phase space available
in scattering processes introducing Fermi factors.
In particular, the kind of lowest order process en-
hancing the electron mass is shown in figure 8. An
electron of momentum $\mathbf{p}$ emits a phonon of momentum
$\mathbf{q}$ scattering to an intermediate state (of higher energy) of momentum $\mathbf{p}' = \mathbf{p} - \mathbf{q}$ and then reabsorbs
this phonon. The intermediate state can only exist
for times of order or shorter than $1/\omega_{\mathbf{q}} \sim \hbar/k_B \theta_D$
from the uncertainty principle since energy is not
conserved. Thus a second order perturbative calculation would yield upon averaging the momentum
over the Fermi surface and picking up a phase space
factor $N(o)$,

$$\lambda = \frac{N(0) \ g^2}{k_B \theta_D} \tag{6}$$

In doing the proper calculation one must include
direct and "exchange processes;" the latter involving
excitations below the Fermi sea (holes). We find because of these two processes that the phonon mass
enhancement occurs only for electrons near (within
$k_B \theta_D$ in energy) of the Fermi surface. For an energy further away the dispersion curve is shifted but
the slope $(dE(k)/dk)$ is unaffected and so m^* (and the
density of states) is not enhanced. In Fig. 9 we plot
schematically the distortion of the Bloch energies
$E(k)$ near E_F from the phonon process shown in figure 8.
The shift far from E_F is a one electron effect analogous

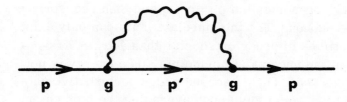

Fig. 8. Lowest order electron-phonon-electron scattering (exchange of phonon) which enhances the electron mass.

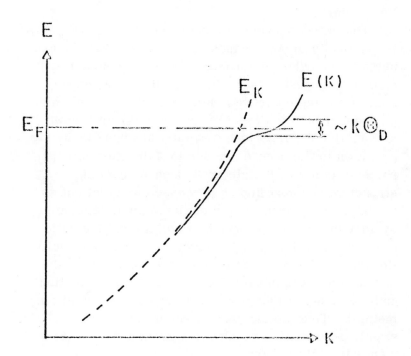

Fig. 9. Many body mass enhancement of electrons near the Fermi surface from electron-phonon interaction. The electron mass and density of states is proportional to $(dE(k)/dk)^{-1}$.

to a polaron in non-metallic crystals, while the change in slope (m^*/m enhancement) near E_F is a true many-body effect because it is sensitive to the distribution of the "other" electrons and so "sees" the Fermi surface.

One might wonder why if the coupling $\lambda(\sim V_{ph}/E_F)$ is near unity in some cases like $Pb(\lambda \sim 1.2)$, one can use second order perturbation theory. Shouldn't higher order processes be included leading to an expansion in g (single vertex). For example, possible higher order processes (vertex corrections) are shown in Fig. 10. When we look carefully at terms involving g^3 shown in this figure, we see that the expansion parameter is not λ, the electron-phonon coupling strength. The next higher processes (corrections to the bare g) as first pointed out by Migdal,[9] are down by an additional factor $\sqrt{m/M}$ which is just the ratio of the sound velocity to the electron (Fermi) velocity. Because of the very retarded (slow) response of the lattice, the electrons adiabatically follows its motion and the higher order processes are not important (in metals). Thus we can take to accuracy $\sqrt{m/M}$ the simple perturbative result for λ given above in (6) and then using (5) we have

$$\lambda = \text{Const.} \frac{N(0) \langle I^2 \rangle}{(\omega_{ph})^2 M} \qquad (7)$$

B. Strong Coupling Theory

When the electron-phonon interaction is strong ($\lambda \sim 1$), the elementary excitations of the metal are not electrons and phonons but some combination. For low excitation energies ($\omega \ll \theta_D$) one can still think

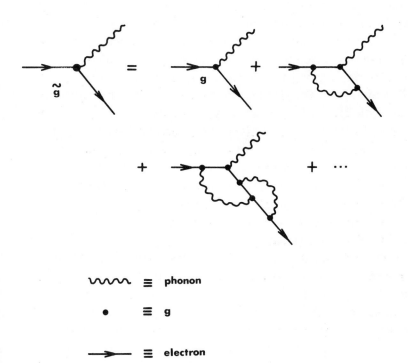

Fig. 10. Expansion of the electron-phonon interaction in terms of higher order corrections to g.
The higher processes are down by the factor
$\sqrt{m/M}$ as discussed in text.

of single particle excitations, which have an energy ω
and momentum $\mathbf{p}$ where

$$\omega_{\mathbf{p}} = \frac{\hbar^2 p^2}{2m} + \Sigma(\mathbf{p}, \omega) \tag{8}$$

$\Sigma(p, \omega)$ is called the self-energy and represents the
many-body effects from phonons and paramagnons and
m is the band-structure mass. In the BCS theory
$\Sigma = 0$, the interactions were taken to be static and only
momentum integrations (giving the phase space for
scattering among Cooper pairs) were carried out.
However, the frequency dependence of the interactions
(and of $\Sigma^\dagger$) is in fact crucial to superconductivity. The
Green's function formalism is a natural way to handle
such time dependent interactions and a full treatment
of the problem require such formalism. We intend
here to only show how such a treatment modifies the
BCS theory and, hopefully, gain some physical in-
sights into the physics of strong-coupling superconductors (as most superconductors with $T_c > 1°K$ really
fall into this category). The mathematical details are
tedious but straightforward and can be found elsewhere,
e.g., in textbooks.[10]

$\Delta(\omega)$ is the strength of the pairing potential for a
quasiparticle of frequency ω, where the momentum
averages have already been made (neglecting aniso-
tropy, etc.). Then $\Delta(\omega)$ depends upon all scattering
processes coupling the particle of frequency ω to other
states (ω') of the system. The structure of the theory
gives for $T_c \lesssim T_c(\Delta \to 0)$ in the weak-coupling limit
(we add to strong coupling features below)

†The very small momentum dependence of Σ is
also an important feature of the normal metal.

$$\Delta(\omega) = - \int_{0}^{\omega_c} \Delta(\omega') K_-(\omega, \omega') d\omega' \qquad (9)$$

where $K_-(\omega, \omega')$ is the total coupling between quasi-particles with frequencies ω and ω', respectively, from the electron-phonon interaction, the Coulomb pseudo-potential and the electron-paramagnon interaction (to be discussed later). First let us consider the electron-phonon interaction. If the electrons are driving the ion oscillators at a given frequency ω then taking a harmonic restoring force for the ions leads to an equation of motion for the ions of the form

$$M\ddot{\overline{X}} + k\overline{X} = A e^{i\omega t} \qquad (10)$$

which has a solution

$$\overline{X} = \frac{A/M}{-\omega^2 + k/M} e^{i\omega t} \qquad (11)$$

Thus if $\omega^2 < k/M$ (i.e., $\omega < \theta_D$)[†] the lattice moves in phase with the electrons driving it and since the electrons and ions are oppositely charged the interaction is attractive. If $\omega^2 > k/M$ the ions move out of phase with the electrons and the interaction is repulsive. Finally when $\omega^2 \gg k/M$ the ions don't move and there is no force.[‡]   This is schematically plotted in Fig. 11.

[†] From now on we work in units where $\hbar = k_B \equiv 1$
[‡] You can see these three regions by studying the behavior of a ball on the end of a flexible spring. Holding the top of the spring and driving the system by moving your hand up and down. For low frequencies the ball follows in phase (with your hand) then as the frequency of the up-down motion increases the ball's motion first goes out of phase and then hardly moves at all.

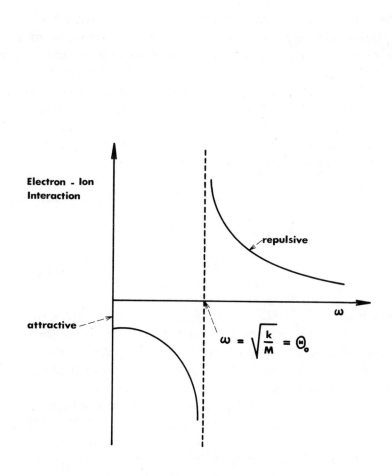

Fig. 11. Schematic plot of electron-ion interaction.

The electron phonon interaction has the same structure as that shown in Fig. 11, except that it depends on the two variables ω and ω'. On the other hand the Coulomb repulsion is almost instantaneous, having a frequency dependency on the scale of E_F rather than θ_D. The different time scales of these two interactions is an important factor in superconductors. The repulsive Coulomb interaction keeps the electrons instantaneously apart which causes a correlation which reduces the overlap of the wavefunctions and thereby reduces the effective Coulomb repulsion that the electrons feel over longer times (low frequencies). Thus since in (9) the integration cut off is at $\omega_c \sim \theta_D$, the effective Coulomb repulsion in this low frequency region is not $\mu = (N(0) V_c)$ but is reduced by the above mentioned correlations to a pseudopotential μ^* where[7],[10]

$$\mu^* = \mu / (1 + \mu \ln E_F / \theta_D) \tag{12}$$

Thus when E_F / θ_D is very large, $\mu^* \to 0 (\lesssim .10)$ while for transition metals where E_F is small (compared with non-transition metals) μ^* is rather large (.15-.20). Still $\mu^* \ll \mu$ and so the high-frequency Coulomb repulsion actually helps the pairing (increases T_c). Also the presence of θ_D in μ^* which enters the exponential coupling changes the isotopic mass dependence of T_c as we will see later. Thus when the frequency dependence of the interactions is properly considered the weak coupling formula (4) is modified giving

$$G = \lambda - \mu^* \tag{13}$$

Even in the normal state the presence of the electron-phonon interaction modifies the electronic properties. In fact, as we have said the new excitations (call them quasiparticles) are not really electrons but some conglomeration of electron and phonon. The amount of phonon in the q.p. is measured by the function $Z(\omega)$ something like

$$\text{fraction of phonon in quasi-particle } 1 - \frac{1}{Z(\omega)}$$

If $Z(0) = 1$ then the q.p. at the Fermi surface is all electron, if $Z(0) = 2$ then its half electron-half phonon. For Pb, $Z(0) = 2.3$ while for most metals $Z(0) \lesssim 1.5$ (which is still a lot); We find that (in the normal state)

$$(1 - Z(\omega))\omega = \int_0^{\omega_c} K_+(\omega, \omega') \, d\omega' \qquad (14)$$

where $K_+(\omega, \omega')$ is just like $K_-(\omega, \omega')$ except that some signs are different and the Coulomb repulsion does not enter—unless it is frequency dependent as when it is large enough to make paramagnons long-lived (more on this later). In fact, integration of (14) yields the simple expression for $Z(0)$

$$Z(0) = 1 + \lambda \qquad (15)$$

Also, we find that the mass-enhancement of the "electron" m^*/m is given by $Z(0)$, i.e.,

$$m^*/m = Z(0) \qquad (16)$$

Thus $Z(\omega)$ describes the many-body effects of the phonons on the electronic system in the "normal" state. Now we must be more careful in deriving the

superconducting pairing between q.p. since they are
only part electron and hence using electronic matrix
elements overestimates the interactions. We simply
renormalize all electronic matrix elements by re-
normalizing the wave functions, i.e.,

$$\psi_{p,\omega} \rightarrow \psi_{p,\omega} / Z(\omega, p) \tag{17}$$

The form of $Z(\omega)$ is shown in Fig. 12, with the characteristic behavior near θ_D and the approach to 1
far above θ_D. If we also enhance the Fermi surface
density of states by $Z(\omega')$ in (9) then remembering
that $K_-^{ph}(\omega, \omega')$ involves a matrix element squared
we find

$$\Delta(\omega) = -\int \Delta(\omega') Z(\omega') \left[\frac{K_-^{ph}(\omega, \omega')}{Z(\omega) Z(\omega')} + \frac{K_-^{coul}(\omega, \omega')}{\sqrt{Z(\omega) Z(\omega')}} \right] d\omega'$$

$$\tag{18}$$

$$= -\frac{1}{Z(\omega)} \int_0^{\omega_c} \Delta(\omega')[K_-^{ph}(\omega, \omega') + \tilde{K}_-^{coul}(\omega, \omega')] d\omega'$$

In $\tilde{K}_-^{coul}(\omega, \omega')$ we dump the high frequency psuedopotential corrections. Very simply since the ω' integration really includes ω' up to E_F where $Z(\omega') \cong 1$
we expect

$$\tilde{K}_-^{coul}(\omega, \omega') \cong \sqrt{Z(\omega)} \, \mu^* \cong (1 + .5\lambda) \mu^*;$$

for $\omega \rightarrow 0$. When solutions of (18) are carried out numerically[6] for a phonon spectrum like that of Nb one
finds the results can be analytically fit by the expression

$$T_c = (\theta_D/1.45)\exp(-1/G) \tag{19}$$

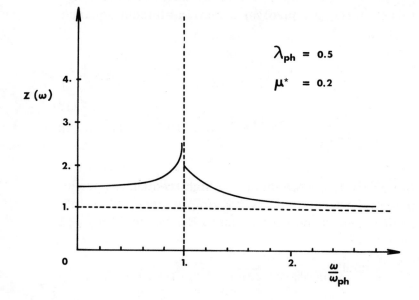

Fig. 12. The frequency dependence of the renormalization parameter (ω) for frequencies
near the characteristic phonon frequency θ_D,
$Z(\omega) \rightarrow 1, \ \omega \rightarrow \infty$.

$$G = \frac{\lambda}{1 + \lambda} - \frac{(1 + .62\lambda)}{1 + \lambda} \, \mu^* \qquad (20)$$

which is just the modification of (13) expected by the renormalization factor $1 + \lambda$. We reiterate that the strong-coupling theory reduces the effective coupling compared with the weak coupling theory by $1/(1 + \lambda)$ because the quasi-particles are renormalized. Only part of them are electron-like and the matrix elements representing the strength of their coupling via phonon-exchange must be corrected. There are, of course, many other strong-coupling effects—e.g., lifetime effects for excitations with $\omega \sim \theta_D$—but in determining $\Delta(0)$ (and hence T_c, assuming $\Delta(0) = 1.75 \, T_c$) we are mainly concerned with the renormalization effects.

Using (16), (19) and (20) and experimental data for θ_D, T_c, and γ we can determine λ and hence using (7) the size of const. $N(0) \langle I^2 \rangle$. This was done by Mc Millan[6] and the results are given in Table I for several elements. (McMillan took $\mu^* = .13$ for the transition elements and .10 for the non-transition elements).

Considering the wide variation of γ (and hence $N(0)$) among the bcc transition elements the near constancy of const. $N(0) \langle I^2 \rangle$ is surprizing. The reason for this is not understood but apparently is due to the extreme sensitivity of the phonon frequencies on the ion pseudopotentials and screening. We simply accept it as an empirical fact and so take for isostructural elements a rough estimate of λ to be given by

$$\lambda = C/M\theta_D^2 \qquad (22)$$

We will return to make use of (22) later in discussing La and the $Z = 3$ metals.

TABLE I: Calculated Const x $N(0) \langle I^2 \rangle$ Values

Element	$\gamma(\text{m joules/mode }^o\text{k}^2)$	Const $N(0) \langle I^2 \rangle$
V (bcc)	9.9	4.6
Nb (bcc)	7.8	7.2
Ta (bcc)	6.0	6.1
Mo (bcc)	1.8	6.8
W (bcc)	0.9	6.3
Al	1.2	2.0
In	1.7	1.8
Pl	3.0	2.3

The isotopic mass dependence of T_c is easily determined from (12), (19) and (20) to be

$$T_c \propto M^{-\alpha}$$

$$\alpha = 1/2 \left[1 - \left(\mu^* \ln \frac{\theta_D}{1.45 T_c} \right)^2 \left(\frac{1 + .62\lambda}{1 + \lambda} \right) \right] \qquad (23)$$

Clearly from (23) deviations of α from $1/2$ are most likely when T_c is small and μ^* is large. This is shown by a plot of α against T_c in Fig. 13; however, the very sharp decrease in α for $T_c \gtrsim 1\,^\circ$K can only be fitted by (23) if μ^* is increasing for those elements. In fact, the elements for which $\alpha \sim 0$ are at the ends ($Z \sim 4, 8$) of the transition metals and thus we find μ^* is increasing there.

This can be seen from Table II where we give the values of μ^* calculated by McMillan.[6]

We might ask how good the theory is in predicting the properties of the transition metals. We can check this for the bcc metals by using the T_c, θ_D, and γ data to determine $N(0)$ and making comparison with the band structure calculations of Matthies.[5] The results[6] are shown in Fig. 14. From the very good agreement found here there is good support for the dominance of phonon-induced superconductivity for the bcc transition metals. However, tunneling data would be very helpful in determining the details of the electron-phonon interaction and the Coulomb psuedopotential, as worked out so beautifully for Pb and other non-Transition metals. However, there remain some questions about other elements-in particular the metals near La, and near Pd. Let us deal with the $Z = 3$ elements near La, first.

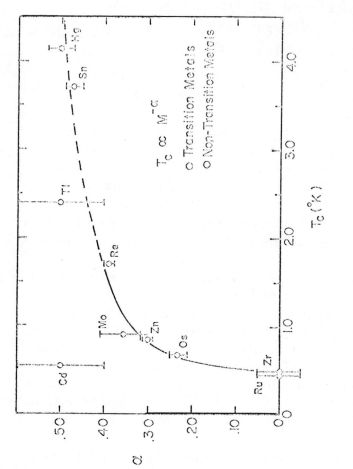

Fig. 13. The variation of the isotopic mass dependence (α) of supercon-ducting transition temperature T_c with the size of T_c.

TABLE II: Calculated Values of the Coulomb Psuedopotential μ^*

Element	Z	α	μ^*
Zr	4	0	.17
Mo	6	.37	.09
Re	7	.38	.10
Ru	8	.21	.12
Og	8	0	.15
Zn	2	.30	.12

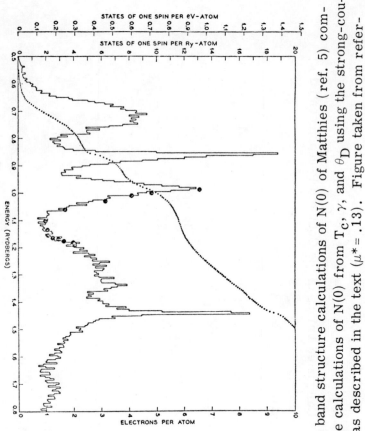

Fig. 14. The band structure calculations of $N(0)$ of Matthies (ref. 5) compared with the calculations of $N(0)$ from T_c, γ, and θ_D using the strong-coupling theory as described in the text ($\mu^* = .13$). Figure taken from reference 6.

C. Superconductivity in La and the Z = 3 Transition Metals

La is superconduting with $T_c = 4.9°K$ (hcp)[†] while the other Z = 3 transition elements Sc, Y, and Lu are not superconducting above $0.01°K$.[1] A number of authors[11] (including the present one) have speculated that the superconductivity in La was not caused by the electron-phonon interaction but was due to another mechanism. However, the Debye temperature θ_D in La is anomolously low compared with the other (Z = 3, 4) hcp transition elements as can be seen from figure 15 where we plot θ_D against $M^{-1/2}$ where M is the nuclear mass. According to (22) the strength of the phonon induced attraction should be inversely proportional to the square of the Debye frequency times the nuclear mass. Thus from Fig. 17 one might expect the electron-phonon interaction in La to be much larger than that in the other hcp metals. The suggestion that this might be the case has been already made by Kasuya and several other authors.[12]

We use McMillan's strong coupling formula (19) and (20) with μ^* taken to be 0.17 which is the value determined from the isotope dependence of T_c for Zr. Then from experimental values for T_c and θ_D for the elements and La-Y alloys given in Table III we can determine λ_{exp}. The La-Y data of Satoh and Ohtsuka[12] is also shown in figure 16.

We determine C in (22) for Zr using the experimental θ_D and M data and using λ_{exp} from above. Using this value of $C(= 3.6 \times 10^6)$ we calculate the value of λ_{theory} (using M and θ_D) for La-Y alloys and

[†]fcc La has $T_c = 6.3°K$

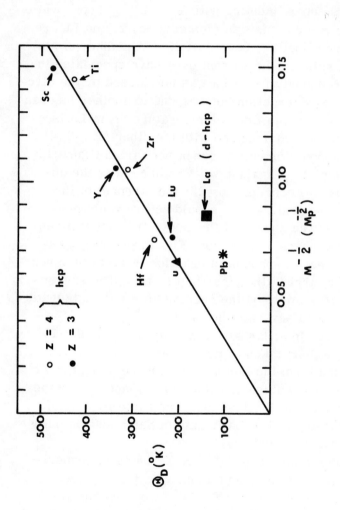

Fig. 15. The variation of the Debye temperature θ_D against nuclear mass M for the Z = 3, 4 transition elements. La is anomolously low indicating a soft lattice and larger electron phonon interaction. Pb and u are included.

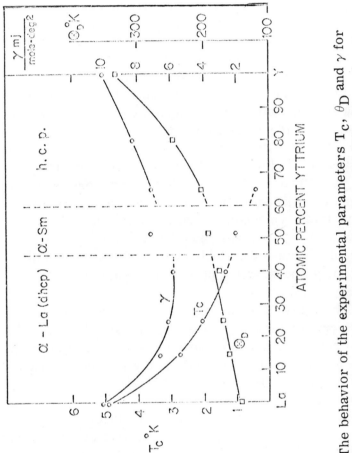

Fig. 16. The behavior of the experimental parameters T_c, θ_D and γ for the La-Y alloy system. Data from work of Satoh and Ohtsuka, reference 12.

for the other hcp elements using (22). The results are given in Table III and are shown in figure 17 where we plot λ_{exp} (Eq. 20) against λ_{theory} (Eq. 22). The agreement is sufficiently good that there seems little doubt that the fall of T_c upon alloying Y with La is due to a decreasing phonon interaction. On the other hand there does appear to be a systematic deviation of λ_{exp} below the theoretical predictions. This is possible evidence for the presence of an additional repulsive interaction for all the Z = 3 elements, as has been noted previously.[13] However, (20) was obtained by McMillan using the Nb(bcc) phonon spectrum and there is no reason to expect it to be quantitatively accurate for hcp metals. We conclude that La is anomalous in its behavior compared with the other Z = 3 elements probably because the electron-phonon interaction is very large (because the phonon frequencies are anomalously small).

The reason for this may be in the proximity to the Fermi surface of the f-electron states[11,12] but there seems little doubt that the mechanism responsible for its superconductivity is the electron-phonon interaction. Evidence for the phonon mechanism being responsible for the superconductivity in La is found in recent tunneling work by Khanna and Rogers.[14] They find some well defined second-derivative structure near the expected phonon-energies. The size of the structure seems about that expected for a strong coupling superconductor (gauged by $T_c/\theta_D)^2$ i.e., roughly 1%).

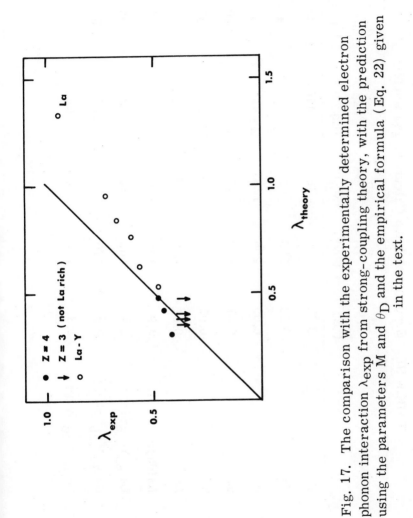

Fig. 17. The comparison with the experimentally determined electron phonon interaction λ_{exp} from strong-coupling theory, with the prediction using the parameters M and θ_D and the empirical formula (Eq. 22) given in the text.

TABLE III: Experimental and Calculated Parameters

Metal	T_C^a (°K)	θ_D^a (°K)	M^b (M_p)	λ_{exp}^c (Eq. 20)	λ_{theory}^d (Eq. 22)
Ti	0.39	426	48	.445	.42
Zr	0.50	289	91	.475	(.475)[d]
Hf	0.09	256	178	.41	.31
Sc	< 0.01	450	45	<.34	.40
Y	< 0.01	330	89	<.35	.37
Lu	< 0.01	210	175	<.35	.47
La(dhcp)	4.9	142	139	.94	1.33
La$_{.85}$Y$_{.15}$(dhcp)	2.7	162	144	.72	.95
La$_{.75}$Y$_{.25}$(dhcp)	2.0	170	148	.67	.84
La$_{.60}$Y$_{.40}$(dhcp)	1.3	175	154	.60	.76

$La_{.48}Y_{.52}(\alpha\text{-}Sm)$	1.0	192	158	.56	.62
$La_{.35}Y_{.65}$	0.4	205	162	.47	.53
$La_{.15}Y_{.85}$	0.1	245	170	$<.40$	.35

a. La-Y data are from reference 12 (Satoh and Ohtsuka)

b. Average mass is used for the alloys

c. λ from (20) using $\mu^* = .17$ as discussed text

d. λ from (22) using the value for Zr to determine $C(=3.6 \times 10^6)$

III. SPIN FLUCTUATIONS IN TRANSITION METALS

A. Introduction

We are interested now in the behavior of the transition temperature near the right end of the 4d and 5d series. In particular we look at the fcc elements (See Fig. 18) and their alloys. The approach we take is to alloy the other elements with Ir (the only superconducting element among them) and study the variation of T_C in the fcc phase. The elements involved are mostly the paramagnetic ones although experiments using the ferromagnetic elements Fe, Co, and Ni are under way and some preliminary results exist.

First we might indicate why we choose the fcc elements in which to look for spin fluctuations. Originally we simply wondered why T_C was so low (below our experimental limit of $0.01\,^\circ$K) in Rh, Pt, and Pd; and so we began studying the properties of the alloys near these elements. I have not said what spin fluctuations are yet and I won't say much for a while but one might expect that as an element becomes closer and closer to being magnetic, i.e., as its magnetic susceptibility increases, this indicates that the Coulomb interaction is increasing and so T_C should decrease. However, as we discussed above, the Coulomb repulsion (μ) being almost instantaneous (time scale $\sim \hbar/E_F$) is very ineffective in suppressing the pairing caused by the very retarded electron-phonon interaction ($\hbar/\theta_D$). However, there are fluctuations in the spin density in a strongly paramagnetic metal which become very long lived and introduce "retarded" repulsive interactions which can effectively inhibit the pairing. The purpose of this lecture is to try to show why we think these spin

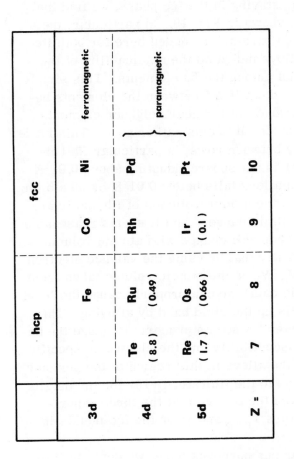

Fig. 18. Superconducting, paramagnetic, and ferromagnetic elements involved in the study of spin fluctuations in the superconducting state in fcc alloys with iridium as the host. The number in parenthesis is the superconducting transition temperature. Rh, Pt, and Pd have been checked for superconductivity experimentally down to $0.01°K$.

fluctuations are responsible for the suppression of T_c near Ir.

If we alloy the neighboring 5d elements (Re, Os, and Pt) with Ir, staying in the fcc phase, we find the variation of T_c shown in Fig. 19. In particular, the fact that Z is the parameter needed here for both Re-Ir and Os-Ir alloys indicated the applicability of the rigid band model among the 5d elements. This simple behavior breaks down if ΔZ between the elements becomes bigger than 3 but for near neighbor elements in the same row (5d) it seems rather good. This model fails if we alloy between rows; in particular Rh (directly above Ir) is not superconducting above 0.01 °K and T_c in Ir-Rh alloys falls below 0.01 °K by 30 atomic % Rh. However, the atomic volumes of Rh and Ir are quite different (Rh is denser) and it seems reasonable that the rigid bands will change with atomic volume. We find empirically that by using the valence electron density $n = Z/V_a$ (V_a is the atomic volume taken from crystallographic data) we can properly gauge the level to which one fills up the rigid band by alloying. This "magic parameter" n seems properly to gauge the behavior of the susceptibility and the electronic specific heat among all the alloys in this region of the periodic table. I refer you to the literature (15) for the details and only show you the behavior of the three experimental parameters T_c, χ and γ for the fcc metals in figure 20.

Actually for our purposes here, we don't need to ask why n is the "right" parameter; we are interested only in the relationship among the three experimental parameters T_c, χ and γ. We see that as one alloys past Ir toward Rh, Pt and Pd that the superconducting transition temperature rapidly falls below our experimental

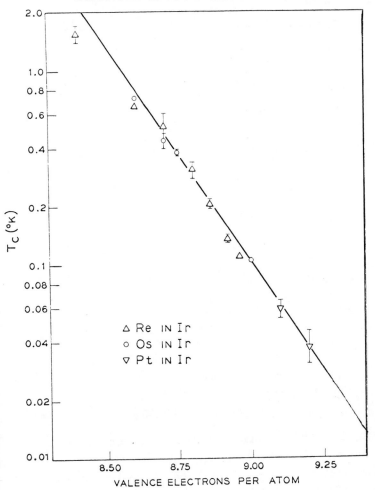

Fig. 19. The variation of T_c in alloys of Ir with other 5d elements as a function of the average number of valence electrons per atom Z. The fact that for Re-Ir and Os-Ir alloys T_c depends only on Z indicates the applicability of the rigid band model for these alloys.

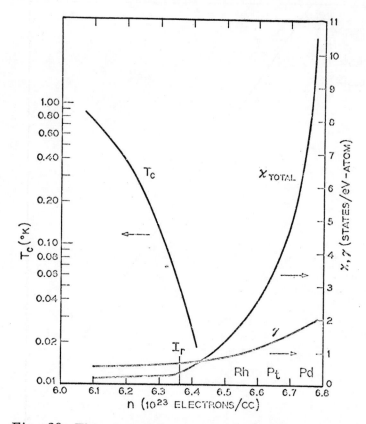

Fig. 20. The variation of the superconducting transition temperature T_c, the electronic specific heat coefficient γ and the magnetic susceptibility χ in the fcc transition metals. The data are for a large number of binary and ternary alloys among the elements Re, Ru, Os, Ir, Rh, Pt, and Pd and are plotted against the valence electrondensity Z/Va, where Va is atomic volume. χ and γ are plotted in units of states/eV-atom (i.e., $\chi/2\mu_B^2$, $3\gamma/\pi^2 k_B^2$). See references 1 and 15.

limit while the magnetic susceptibility very abruptly
begins increasing. If there were no electron-electron
interactions then we would have $\chi = \gamma$ (in these units)
and so the fact that $\chi \gg \gamma$ for alloys near Pd indicates
that electron-electron interactions are very important.
In particular, the Coulomb interaction (and hence as
we shall see – also the importance of the spin fluctuations) is increasing rapidly as we near Pd. This, we
believe, is what is ultimately suppressing the superconducting pairing in these metals. A rough extrapolation of T_c indicates that Pd should not superconduct
even at $0\,^\circ$K and Rh and Pt should at most have T_c
roughly $10^{-3}\,^\circ$K.

Now let us turn our attention to the properties of
strongly paramagnetic ($\chi \gg \gamma$) metals. We want to
understand why such metals have their superconducting pairing so strongly inhibited and hopefully quantitatively explain the suppression of T_c for the above
alloy systems. First we might ask what happens as χ
goes to infinity. One can achieve this by adding Ni to
Pd or Rh. The behavior of χ and γ for this latter system is shown in Fig. 21. (Neither Ni nor Rh is superconducting above our experimental limit, $0.01\,^\circ$K.)
We see that there is a critical concentration above
which the alloys are ferromagnetic (63 at % Ni). We
are interested in what happens in the alloys as one
approaches this concentration from the paramagnetic
side. In particular does the Ni atom have a magnetic
moment associated with it, does it just increase the
local susceptibility (because of the local Coulomb and
exchange interaction), or does it simply increase the
bulk susceptibility of the alloy in some average uniform way. We will find that in many respects there
is no precise distinction between any of these pictures

and that the most appropriate one depends upon the
temperature and the time scale with which one is concerned. If the Ni atoms went into the Rh host as "magnetic" impurities which behaved as "free spins" they
would show a strongly temperature dependent susceptibility (like a Curie law). In Fig. 22 we show the temperature dependence of the susceptibility for a series
of the Rh-Ni alloys. We see that there is essentially
no temperature dependence of χ for the low Ni concentration alloys. However, even for these alloys the
Pauli-like susceptibility is very much increased over
the pure Rh value, as we can see from looking back at
Fig. 21. On the other hand as we increase the Ni concentration and approach the critical concentration (63%)
there appears a stronger and stronger temperature dependence and very near the instability it resembles a
Curie-Weiss type of susceptibility. How can we tell
there are no local-magnetic moments on the Ni sites
in this region? The leveling off of χ for low temperatures could in principle be caused by random antiferromagnetic ordering of local moments with ferromagnetism occurring above 63% Ni. Mossbauer experiments or nuclear magnetic resonance (NMR) linewidth
experiments can resolve this question but they have not
been carried out on these alloys. However, there is
work of this kind on other systems (e.g., Cu-Fe) which
will be discussed below.

    If one adds Fe to Ir, Rh or Cu we find a quantita-
tively different behavior to that of Ni in Rh. For Fe
alloys the increase in the susceptibility is much more
rapid with concentration. For example $1/\chi \, (d\chi/dc)$ for
Rh Ni is 12 while for Ir -Fe it is 600. Also the temperature dependence of the susceptibility is large for low

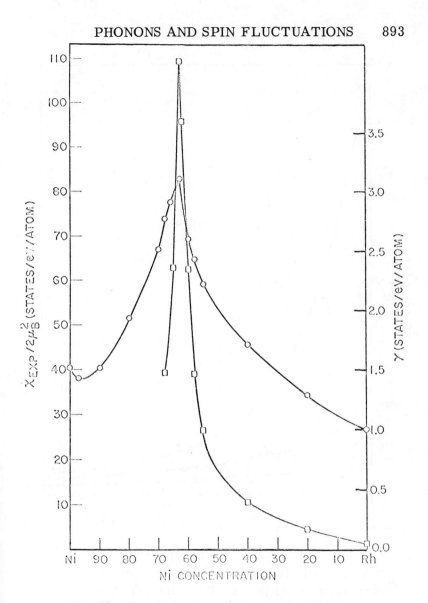

Fig. 21. The behavior of the susceptibility χ and electron specific heat γ for the Rh-Ni system. For concentrations of Ni larger than 63 and % the alloys are ferromagnetic. The data are from reference 16.

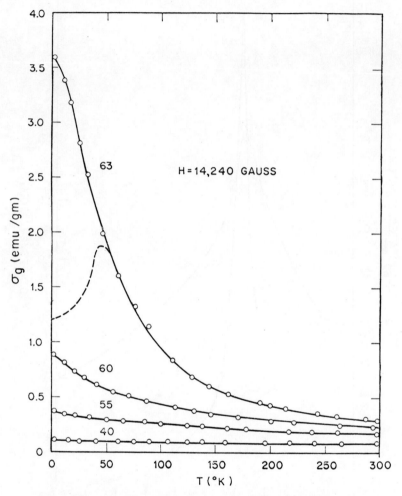

Fig. 22. The temperature dependence of the susceptibility ($\chi = \sigma/H$) for Rh-Ni alloys for various concentrations. The numbers labelling the curves are the atomic percentage of Ni. For greater than 63% Ni the alloys are ferromagnetic. Data are from reference 16.

concentrations. For example, in Fig. 23a, b we show the temperature dependence of χ for R̲h̲-Fe and Ir-Fe alloys.[17] We see that the increase in the susceptibility is linear in concentration (we plot $\Delta\chi/c$) and that the temperature dependence is qualitatively similar to that seen above in the Rh-Ni system if one chooses the appropriate concentration near enough to the critical one. The data for the CuFe system are of the same form with a Curie-Weiss dependence (the Curie constant is however, independent of concentration) for data at high temperatures ($> 40\,°K$) and levels off becoming eventually temperature independent (and for low magnetic fields also field independent; i.e., $M = \chi H$, $\chi = $ const). Thus the low temperature susceptibility has the same behavior for all these systems as is shown schematically in Fig. 24.

The question which we raised is, what is the microscopic picture on the impurities (and around them)? In particular, is there a moment on the impurity or more precisely, is $\langle S_{z\ local}\rangle \neq 0$, in zero external field. If $\langle S_{z\ local}\rangle \neq 0$ then there are local moments and the alloy has some random ordering. If $\langle S_{z\ local}\rangle = 0$, then we have no net moment on the impurity. We want to show that this later case is the actual one involved in the systems we are studying. We can not make such a determination from bulk susceptibility, but Mossbauer experiments (on the Fe nucleus) and NMR linewidths measure $\langle S_{z\ local}\rangle$. In Fig. 25 we show schematically what the field dependence of $\langle S_{z\ local}\rangle$ should look like for a free spin and also a magnetic moment in a randomly ordered crystal. The results found by NMR linewidth[18] and Mossbauer experiments[19] on CuFe alloys we show schematically for comparison. From these results we see that at low

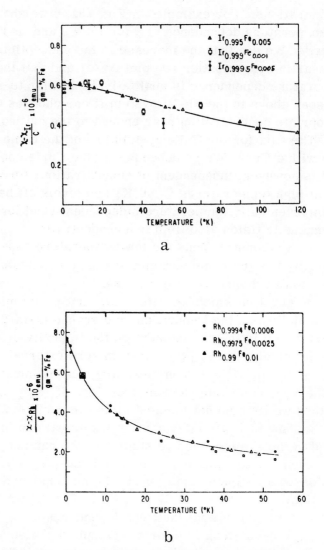

Fig. 23. Temperature dependence of the susceptibility per impurity $\Delta\chi/c$ for Ir-Fe(a) and Rh-Fe alloys. Data are from reference 17.

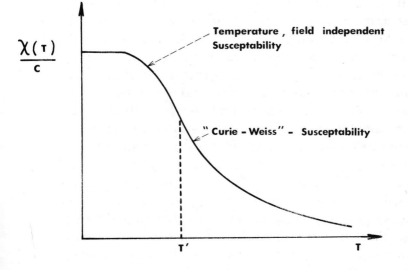

Fig. 24. Schematic temperature dependence of
the susceptibility for Fe in Ir, Rh, Cu, etc., where
T' ~ 100 °K, 3 °K, and 15 °K, respectively.

temperatures we really have no net local moments on the impurities. As we apply a magnetic field however the metal gradually polarizes and its response is much stronger (χ is larger) than for the pure metal. Comparing the NMR and Mossbauer experiments with the bulk susceptibility indicates that part of the polarization is local and part is spread out in the conduction electrons around the impurity. Thus as we apply a field we do develop (gradually) a local moment but this is true in any transition metal alloy, e.g., in Ir-Pd the Pd ion developes a much greater (10 times) magnetization than the Ir ion in the same external field. On the other hand in pure Pd the polarization must be the same on each ion because the interactions on each site are the same and so we think in terms of a uniform model. Thus we have several different models with which we can study the effects of strong paramagnetism upon the superconducting pairing interaction. Below we will discuss these models in a little more detail and then show the general behavior expected of such systems and in particular discuss the properties of the spin fluctuations which modify so many experimental properties. We find that we can make some predictions independent of the model and so we will concentrate on discussing the actual calculations using only the simple uniform interaction model. Our goal is to find relationships among the variation (upon alloying) of the three experimental parameters χ, γ, and T_c. What we will find is that both theoretically and experimentally these relationships are very nearly model independent.

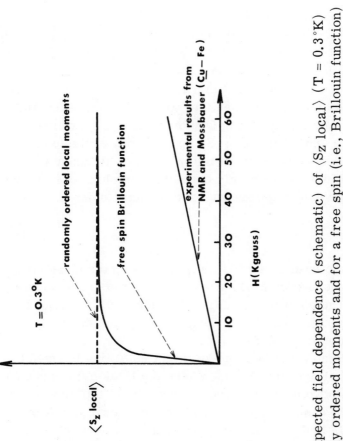

Fig. 25. Expected field dependence (schematic) of $\langle S_z \text{ local}\rangle$ ($T = 0.3\,^\circ K$) for randomly ordered moments and for a free spin (i.e., Brillouin function) compared with the experimental results from NMR linewidth and Mossbauer experiments. For experimental data see references 18 and 19.

B. Theoretical Models

1) Uniform Model
Consider a metal like Pd having d electrons which
move from ion to ion but are rather tightly bound on a
given ion and s electrons which occupy mostly the space
between the ions. So the d electrons are shielded from
each other except when they are on the same ion and
then they feel a strong Coulomb repulsion (we use a
single orbital model). Since the Pauli exclusion keeps
parallel spins apart, if the interaction is taken as a
delta function then only opposite spin electrons interact
and we can write the interaction hamiltonian as

$$\mathcal{H}' = I_0 \int d^3x \, n\!\uparrow\!(\vec{x}) \, n\!\downarrow\!(\vec{x}) \qquad (24)$$

We see intuitively that as I_0 increases the expectation
of the operator $n\!\uparrow\!(x) \, n\!\downarrow\!(x)$ will decrease and when I_0
is large enough $(I_0 > E_F)$ the metal will undergo a ferromagnetic instability such that each ion develops a
net moment ($\langle n\!\uparrow\! n\!\downarrow\!\rangle = 0$).

Such a uniform model might (20) also be used to
treat alloys, like Ir-Rh, where the Coulomb interaction
on the two different types of ions is not too dissimilar.
In that case we simply replace the interaction at every
site I_0 by $I_0 + c\,\delta I$. We neglect the "valence effects,"
assuming the dominant effects are from the exchange
scattering, which is not obviously a good approximation in alloys between elements which are not isoelec-
tronic (same Z), but which does seem to contain most
of the physics.

2) Local Exchange Enhanced Impurity Model

When very strongly exchange-enhanced impurities are added to a metal it seems more reasonable to treat them as introducing locally large perturbations in I with the host ions having an unhanged interaction I_0. In this case we modify (24) by adding the term[21]

$$\Delta \mathcal{H} = \Delta I \sum_{\substack{\text{impurities}}} n_{i\uparrow} n_{i\downarrow} \qquad (25)$$

In this case since $\Delta I > I_0$ (e.g., $I_0 = 0$ for Ru-Fe and CuFe alloys) the impurities can become magnetic first before the host atoms if for example, one could increase the Fermi surface density of states $N(0)$. Then one would have localized moments. In this case the electrons moving through the crystal will interact with the localized spins and we use a different Hamiltonian.

3) Magnetic Impurity Model

The Hamiltonian most often used to treat the interaction of conduction electrons of spin density $\vec{s}(\vec{x})$ with a localized impurity spin $\vec{S}$ is the Heisenberg contact interaction[22]

$$\mathcal{H}(x) = J \sum_i \vec{s}(\vec{x}) \cdot \vec{S} \, \delta(\vec{x} - \vec{x}_i) \qquad (26)$$

The effects of such an interaction on the properties of a metal are truly remarkable in particular one finds a breakdown of perturbation theory at temperatures below the "Kondo temperature" T_K where[18]

$$T_K = E_F \exp[-1/N(0)J] \qquad (27)$$

Far below this temperature the impurity spin is coupled with the conduction electrons in a many-body singlet state with a binding energy $\sim k_B T_K$.[23] As one applys a field, since only a few degrees of freedom are involved in this quasibound state the singlet is gradually polarized until somewhat above a "critical field" $H_c(\sim k_B T_K/\mu_B)$ the singlet is broken up and the impurity spin aligns completely in the field. In CuFe and Ir -Fe and the other systems of interest here if this model is appropriate $T_K \gg 1\,°K$ and so in treating the superconducting state we are always at temperatures far below T_K. In this case, as we saw above experimentally we cannot distinguish from the bulk susceptibility between any of these three models. In fact, we will find experimentally that the relationships among the three experimental parameters of interest, T_c, χ and γ, are qualitatively independent of the model. As far as things have been worked out theoretically this should be the case. Below we will discuss at some length the properties expected of a system described by the uniform model (3.1) and then mention how calculations for the local model (3.2) differ (the differences are very small). We will also argue that the results using the third model (3.3) should not be very different in the region ($T \ll T_K$) appropriate for our alloys.

Our goal in this part of the paper is to determine what the relationships should be among the experimental parameters; $(1/\chi)\,d\chi/dc$, $(1/T_c)\,dT_c/dc$ and $(1/\gamma)\,d\gamma/dc$. We then will show how the theoretical predictions agree (or disagree) with experiment. First however we will try to develop some physical feeling for the properties expected of strongly paramagnetic metals.

C. Strongly Paramagnetic Metals–Spin Fluctuations

When we apply a magnetic field to a metal a magnetization is produced which we describe in fourier transformed $\mathbf{q}$, and ω space by $\chi(\mathbf{q}, \omega)$ where (assuming only local interactions)

$$M(\mathbf{q}, \omega) = \chi(\mathbf{q}, \omega)\ H(\mathbf{q}, \omega) \qquad (28)$$

$\chi(\mathbf{q}, \omega)$ describes the magnetic response of the metal in the same way that $\epsilon(q, \omega)$, the dielectric function, describes the electric response of the metal. We can determine the space-time response $\chi(\mathbf{r}, t)$ by applying a field at $r = t = 0$ and then removing it. Then $\chi(\mathbf{r}, t)$ tells us the way that the moment $M(r = 0, t = 0)$ "propagates" in the metal, i.e.,

$$\chi(\mathbf{r}, t) \propto \langle [M(\mathbf{r}, t), M(0, 0)] \rangle \qquad (29)$$

In terms of electron operators we have for the transverse susceptibility

$$\chi^{-+}(\mathbf{r}, t) = \langle [\sigma(\mathbf{r}, t)\sigma^{+}(0, 0)] \rangle \qquad (30)$$

where $\sigma^{+}(\mathbf{r}, t) = \psi^{+}_{\uparrow}(\mathbf{r}, t)\ \psi_{\downarrow}(\mathbf{r},)$ and the ground state wave functions are used in evaluating the expectation value in (30). Schematically we can represent this "propagation" χ^{-+} by diagrams. The operator $\sigma^{-}(r, t)$ $\sigma^{+}(0, 0)$ means that we scatter an electron from a spin down to a spin up state at $r = t = 0$ and then ask for the probability that we can scatter one from spin up to spin down at r, t. In $\mathbf{q}$, ω space we draw the diagrams shown in Fig. 26. Thus, the susceptibility in the interacting system is

$$\chi(\mathbf{q}, \omega) = \chi_0(\mathbf{q}, \omega) / (1 - I \chi_0(\mathbf{q}, \omega)) \qquad (31)$$

$\chi_0(\mathbf{q}, \omega)$ is given by

$$\chi_0(\mathbf{q}, \omega) \propto \sum_k \frac{f_{k+q} - f_k}{\epsilon_{k+q} - \epsilon_k + \omega}$$

$$\chi_0(\mathbf{q}, 0) \equiv \chi_0 \, u(\mathbf{q})$$

$$\chi_0 \equiv 2\mu_B^2 N(0) \qquad (32)$$

$$u(\mathbf{q}) \cong 1/(1 + \frac{1}{3} (q/2k_F)^2); \ q \lesssim k_F$$

Physically it is clear that repulsive interactions among the opposite spin electrons keep them apart which means an effective attraction of an electron and hole of opposite spin–thus as I increases the electron-hole excitation shown in Fig. 26 "sticks" together longer and longer (in r and t) and eventually at the ferromagnetic instability ($\chi_0 I = 1$) the "pair" is fully bound. Before one reaches the instability the system can locally fluctuate into the p-h "bound state" and these fluctuations have many effects on the properties of the system.

There is a fundamental theorem in statistical mechanics—first derived in general by Callen and Welton[24]—called the fluctuation-dissipation theorem which relates the fluctuations expected in a system to the dissipation under an external perturbation. Since the response and dissipation are related by the Kramers-Kronig relations, we then can use this theorem to completely determine the fluctuations of a system

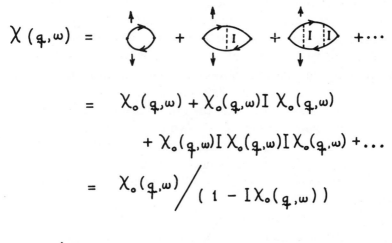

$$\chi(q,\omega) = \text{(diagrams)}$$

$$= \chi_0(q,\omega) + \chi_0(q,\omega) I \chi_0(q,\omega)$$

$$+ \chi_0(q,\omega) I \chi_0(q,\omega) I \chi_0(q,\omega) + \dots$$

$$= \chi_0(q,\omega) \Big/ (1 - I\chi_0(q,\omega))$$

$\uparrow \longrightarrow \equiv$ up spin electron

$\downarrow \longleftarrow \equiv$ down spin hole

Fig. 26. Diagrams representing the effect of electron-electron interactions (I) on the susceptibility. The first term is just the excitation (at $r = t = 0$) of a particle from the up spin band to the down spin band and its subsequent (at r, t) de-excitation. This "measures" the response of the metal to a $\delta(r)\,\delta(t)$ spin polarization. The interactions (I) make the residual response at r, t larger and finally at $I\chi_0$ $(0, 0) = 1$ there is a ferromagnetic instability.

given the response. In our case the magnetic response is defined completely by the complex function $\chi(\mathbf{q}, \omega)$ defined in (28). In the same way Nozieres and Pines[25] developed a complete treatment of the electron gas from the dielectric function $\epsilon(\mathbf{q}, \omega)$, we can do the same for the magnetic properties using $\chi(\mathbf{q}, \omega)$. In general, of course, we don't know the whole functional form of $\chi(\mathbf{q}, \omega)$ for all $\mathbf{q}$ and ω, but we can calculate it for certain model problems. [We can determine part of $\chi(q, \omega)$ from experimental results, as we will discuss below]. For example, in a uniform model in which we use $\mathcal{H}'$ given in (24) we expect as discussed above, that the space and time response will grow longer as $\chi_0 I$ approaches unity. Thus the real part of $\chi(\mathbf{q}, 0)$ and $\chi(0, \omega)$ should look schematically as shown in Fig. 27. The characteristic length is given by $l_S \equiv (1/k_F)S$ and the time by $t_S \equiv (h/E_F)S$, where S is the Stoner factor; $S = \chi/\chi_0 = (1 - I\chi_0)^{-1}$ and we use the convention that $\chi(q = 0, \omega = 0) \equiv \chi$, $\chi_0(q = 0, \omega = 0) \equiv \chi_0$.

We can check these ideas experimentally, e.g., by placing a local magnetic perturbation in a metal which is near the f.m.i. If we place an iron atom in Pd($S \approx 10$) then we will be measuring the effect of a $\delta(r)$ (constant in time) perturbation; hence

$$\chi(\mathbf{r}, \omega = 0) = \int_0^\infty \chi(\mathbf{r}, t) \, dt \qquad (33)$$

Such experiments are done by neutron-elastic scattering and results for Pd-Fe are shown schematically in Fig. 28. Note that the characteristic fall off distance near the impurity of the host spin polarization is $\sim 5\mathring{A}$ which is roughly an order of magnitude larger than $1/k_F$ and this is qualitatively consistent with

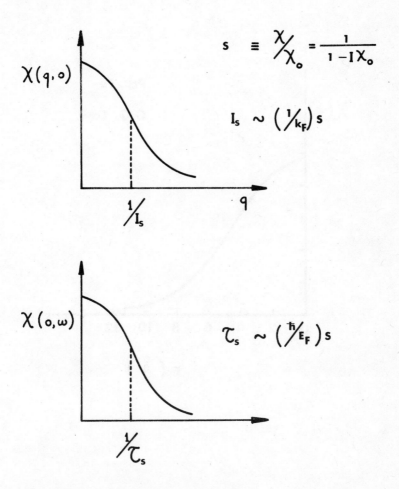

$$s \equiv \frac{\chi}{\chi_0} = \frac{1}{1 - I\chi_0}$$

$$I_s \sim \left(\frac{1}{k_F}\right) s$$

$$\tau_s \sim \left(\frac{\hbar}{E_F}\right) s$$

Fig. 27. Schematic representation of $\chi(q, 0)$ and $\chi(0, \omega)$ giving the space and time response to a magnetic perturbation as one nears the ferromagnetic instability.

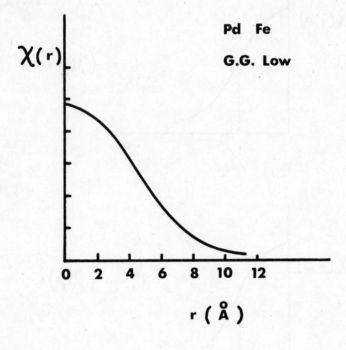

Fig. 28. Susceptibility of Pd about a local magnetic perturbation (Fe), showing the long range
of the spatial response for a metal with S ~ 10.
Data for G.G. Low Proc. Int. Conf. on Magnetism,
Nottingham (Sept. 1964) p. 133.

S $\cong 10$ for pure Pd. In figure 29 we show χ $(\mathbf{q}, 0)$ and $\chi_0(\mathbf{q}, 0)$. The discontinuity in $\chi_0(\mathbf{q}, 0)$ at $2k_F$ is a characteristic feature of p-h excitations since $2k_F$ is the maximum possible momentum transfer for $\omega = 0$ excitation. This discontinuity in q space introduces the familiar oscillations in real space known as RKKY oscillations. It is these oscillations (in spin density in the electron liquid) which are proportional to $\langle S_{z\ local} \rangle$ and which we measured by the NMR linewidth experiments discussed in IIIA. Using $\chi_0(\mathbf{q}, 0)$ given in (32) and using (31) with $\chi_0 I = .9$ (S = 10) we have plotted $\chi(\mathbf{q}, 0)$ in Fig. 29.

When a metal is strongly paramagnetic (S $\gg$ 1) physically it is not far from going ferromagnetic because the kinetic energy it costs for an electron to pair with an opposite spin hole (in real space) is almost balanced by the lowering of the potential energy from the decreased Coulomb interaction. Since the energy difference is getting smaller as one nears $S = \infty$($I\chi_0 = 1$) the uncertainty principle allows such a binding to occur for longer and longer times so $\tau_S = \hbar/(E_F - I) = (\hbar/E_F)S$. As in the case of phonons in a metal these spin fluctuations or paramagnons introduce frequency dependent effects and modify the electron mass and the superconducting pairing interaction. We can get an idea of the frequency distribution of the paramagnons from the schematic plots of Im$\chi(\mathbf{q}, \omega)$ shown in Fig. 30, b,c,d,e,f. Here we show a dispersion curve $\omega \propto q$ from a pure undamped excitation and the spectral distribution (with δ function sharpness) associated with it. The paramagnon excitations are strongly damped by interactions with the one particle continuum and so the dispersion curve is broadened as shown schematically in figure 30c, d (S = 1)

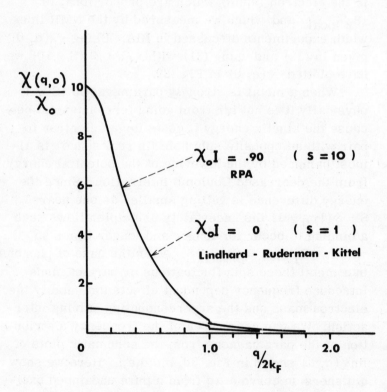

Fig. 29. Momentum dependence of statis ($\omega = 0$) susceptibility for non-interacting electrons χ_0 (q, 0) (S = 1) and for a metal like Pd χ(q, 0) (S $\cong$ 10).

and thus the spectral distribution is very broad. However, as the strength of the Coulomb repulsion increases the velocity of propagation (i.e., the slope of the ω - q curve) decreases as v_F/S and so the spectral weight moves lower in frequency with the characteristic frequency at which $Im\chi(k_F, \omega)$ peaks being given roughly by E_F/S (see Fig. 30e, f). There are, of course, excitations of lower frequency present for small q for which the characteristic peak frequency is $\omega_q = qv_F/S$. Since for superconductivity the important attraction from phonons comes at frequencies less than the characteristic lattice response frequency $\hbar/k_B\theta_D$ we expect spin fluctuations which lead to p-h correlations unfavorable to superconductivity to become very important in superconductors when $E_F/S < k_B\theta_D$, i.e., for metals in which $S > E_F/\theta_D \sim 10$ to 100 in transition metals. In fact, we will find that the low q, low ω spin fluctuations-paramagnons are effective enough in inhibiting superconductivity that even for S much smaller than E_F/θ_D the pairing can be completely inhibited.

From the above discussion it is clear that a knowledge of $\chi(q, \omega)$ is completely sufficient to determine the paramagnetic response and properties of a metal. Unfortunately we can only at present determine experimentally certain portions of $\chi(q, \omega)$. For example, bulk susceptibility measures $\chi(q = 0, \omega = 0)$. But one must also have the functional form of $\chi(q, \omega)$ to be able to predict the electron mass (specific heat) enhancement and superconducting transition temperature suppression. Of course, the other properties are dependent upon $\chi(q, \omega)$ (e.g., nuclear magnetic relaxation time, transport properties, etc.) but they are outside the scope of this paper. Alternatively, one can determine the

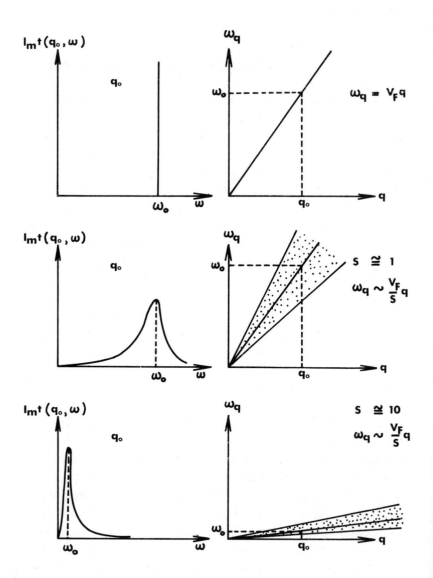

$$^t\text{PP}(\ \mathbf{q}, \omega\ ) =$$

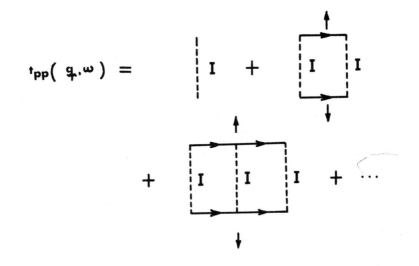

Fig. 30. Schematic dispersion relations and spectral distribution functions for undamped boson ᐧxcitation (phonon, Einstein model) (a. and b.); for paramagnons with weak interactions (c. and d.); and for paramagnons with strong interactions (S ≅ 10, like Pd metal.)

functional form expected for $\chi(q, \omega)$ for a given model problem (see IIIB) and then parameterize the function with $\chi(q = 0, \omega = 0)$ taken from experiments. We will find below that some predictions from such an analysis would appear to be model independent.

First we might ask how electrons interact via the emission and absorption of paramagnons. If we return to the multiple scattering picture of two electrons of opposite spin k ↑ and k' ↓ interacting via I, we find using the diagrams given in figure 30 that the multiple particle-particle scattering when summed to all orders, which we call $t_{pp}(q, \omega)$, can be written

$$t_{pp}(\mathbf{q}, \omega) = I/(1 + I\chi_0(\mathbf{q}, \omega)) \qquad (34)$$

Clearly no instability in the system occurs because of the plus sign in the denominator. This is because the interaction is repulsive and so merely keeps the particles further apart as it increases in strength. This is why it is not the particle-particle (opposite spin) scattering which leads to the f.m.i. It is reminiscent of work in superconductivity in which no instability can occur for purely repulsive interactions, because merely by pushing electrons apart one can never acquire any macroscopic coherence.[26] In this case we see a similar situation. The pushing apart of opposite spin electrons when considered to all orders just introduced a "correlation" among them such that I is replaced by $I_{eff} \sim (1/2)I$, (for $N(0)I \sim 1$) and nothing fancy happens. However, if we consider the interaction between an electron and a hole of opposite spin, they attract and so, it is correlations built up from multiple scattering of an opposite spin electron hole pair that lead to the binding which finally produces the ferromagnetic instability. Thus the diagrams of importance are not those shown in Fig. 30 but those in Fig. 31. Summing these diagrams we find

$$t_{ph} (\mathbf{q}, \omega) = I^* / (1 - I^* \chi_0 (q, \omega)) \tag{35}$$

We use I^* instead of I because the multiple particle-particle scattering will introduce correlations between the electrons which reduce the Born p-h term. Actually nothing very precise can be done in getting from I to I^* except in the very low density limit when $I^* = t_{pp}(0, 0)$.[27] Therefore, henceforth we will drop the star. This conforms with the previous formulas for $\chi(q, \omega)$. By comparing figure 31 and 26 and (31) and (35) we see that $t_{p-h}(q, \omega)$ is just the stuff inside the bubbles, in fact

$$\chi(\mathbf{q}, \omega) = t_{p-h}(\mathbf{q}, \omega) \left(\frac{\chi_0(\mathbf{q}, \omega)}{I} \right) \tag{36}$$

In III we showed how the phonon many body effects were measured by the dimensionless parameter λ_{ph} which was $N(0)g^2/\omega_{ph}$ as one might have guessed from second order perturbation theory for the lowest order electron-electron interaction due to exchange of a phonon. Actually the calculation of the mass enhancement involved an integral over the frequency distribution of the phonons given by the spectral distribution of the phonons (given by Im $D_\lambda(q, \omega)$)[10] which is anologous to the spectral distribution of spin fluctuations Im $t(q, \omega)$ shown in figure 30. If we consider the paramagnon excitation for an electron on the Fermi surface for momentum, frequency transfer q, ω we have in a second order perturbative argument, averaging over the Fermi surface.

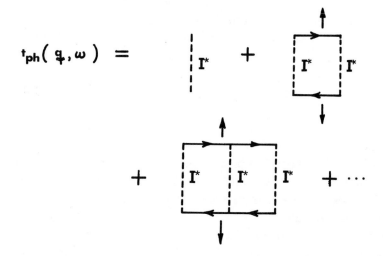

Fig. 31. Particle-particle opposite spin multiple scattering t-matrix $t_{pp}(\mathbf{q}, \omega)$. No instability appears as $I \to \infty$ as can be seen from (34). Since the interaction is repulsive the effect of the multiple scattering is to introduce correlations which keep the particles apart.

$$\Delta E \propto \int_0^{2k_F} \frac{qdq}{2k_F} \left[\int_{-\infty}^{\mu} (-d\omega'') N(0) I \frac{Imt(\mathbf{q}, \omega'')}{\omega''} \right.$$

$$+ \int_{\mu}^{\infty} d\omega'' N(0) I \left. \frac{Imt(q, \omega'')}{\omega''} \right]$$

$$\propto \int_0^{2k_F} \frac{qdq}{2k_F} Re\, t(q, 0) \tag{37}$$

where the last step has been made using a Kramers-Kronig type relation

$$Re\, t(\mathbf{q}, \omega) = \frac{P}{\pi} [\int_{\mu}^{\infty} - \int_{-\infty}^{\mu}] d\omega'' \frac{Imt(\mathbf{q}, \omega'')}{\omega'' - \omega} \tag{38}$$

using (32) and (36) we find for the dimensionless parameter giving the strength of the paramagnon coupling λ_{spin}

$$\lambda_{spin} = \frac{9}{2} \ln \frac{S}{3} . \tag{39}$$

The analysis here is essentially the same as for phonons so there is no surprize that the results are similar. In particular we have

$$T_c \cong \theta_D e^{-1/g} \tag{40}$$

$$g = \frac{\lambda_{ph} - \lambda_{spin} - \mu^*}{1 + \lambda_{ph} + \lambda_{spin}} \tag{42}$$

$$m^*/m = 1 + \lambda_{ph} + \lambda_{spin} \tag{43}$$

where λ is defined in (40).

D. Experimental Properties

We are interested in the concentration dependence of χ, T_c and γ as one adds impurities which are strongly paramagnetic. We can treat the problem in the uniform model by changing I_0 to $I = I_0 + c\,\delta I$ at every site and assuming translational invariance. (See Section III B1). On the other hand we could retain the local model (see Section III B2) features by changing I_0 to $(I_0 + \Delta I)$ at only the cN impurity sites and then being careful to treat the scattering on each site without momentum conservation. These two approaches lead to very different $Imt(q, \omega)$ functions. However, the properties measured here, T_c and γ, depend upon integrals over q, ω and so may not be very sensitive to where (e.g.) as a function of ω the spectral weight lies. The experimental parameters of interest are

$$R_1 \equiv \frac{g^2 \chi_{host}}{T_c^{host}} \frac{dT_c}{d\chi} \tag{44}$$

$$R_2 \equiv \frac{g^2 \gamma_{host}}{T_c^{host}} \frac{dT_c}{d\gamma} \tag{45}$$

$$R_1/R_2 \equiv \frac{\chi_{host}}{\gamma_{host}} \frac{d\gamma}{d\chi} \tag{46}$$

$$c^* \equiv \text{f.m.i. critical concentration} \tag{47}$$

The reason for defining these parameters will become clear below. The theoretical results (28, 29) for R_1, R_2, R_1/R_2, and c^* are

1. Uniform Model

$$R_1 = 3/2 \; m/m^* \; \frac{I_0 \chi_0}{1 - I_0 \chi_0}$$

$$R_2 = 1$$

$$c^* = 1/\left(\frac{1}{\chi_{host}} \; \frac{d\chi}{dc} \right)$$

(48)

2. Local Model

$$R_1 = 3/2 \; m/m^* \; \frac{f(I_0, \Delta I)}{1 - I_0 \chi_0} \quad (f \cong .5)$$

$$R_2 = 1$$

$$c^* = 1/\left(\frac{1}{\chi_{host}} \; \frac{d\chi}{dc} \right)$$

(49)

Thus although we see that there is a slight difference in R_1 (not different by more than a factor of 2, in most alloys) the two models predict the same expression for R_2 and c^*.

The existing experimental results[29] are shown in Table IV, where we have data for samples with $(1/\chi)$ $d\chi/dc$ ranging over 4 decades. In Figure 31 we have

M. ANTHONY JENSEN

TABLE IV: Experimental Data

Alloy System	$\dfrac{1}{\chi}\dfrac{d\chi}{dc}$	$-\dfrac{1}{T_c}\dfrac{dT_c}{dc}$	$\dfrac{1}{\gamma}\dfrac{d\gamma}{dc}$	g
$\underline{Ir}$-Rh	4.3	4.0		0.120
$\underline{Ir}$-Pt	5.2	3.1	0.23	0.120
$\underline{Ir}$-Pd	8.1	6.9		0.120
$\underline{Ir}_{70}$-Os_{30}-Fe	250	(186)[j]		0.145
$\underline{Ir}$-Fe	600	(1400)	49.1	0.12
$\underline{Ru}$-Fe	12.6	37	2.7	0.140
$\underline{Rh}$-Ni	12.1		1.3	
$\underline{Pd}$-Ni	87		15	
Cu-Fe	15000		1100	
Al-Mn	97	560	32	0.170

a.   see reference 30

b.   see reference 31

c.   see reference 32

d.   see reference 33

e.   see reference 34

R_1	R_2	R_1/R_2	c^*	$\frac{1}{\chi}\frac{d\chi}{dc}$	Ref.
0.013			> 1	0.23	a
0.008	0.19	0.044	> 1	0.19	a
0.012			> 1	0.12	a
(0.016)			> 0.01	0.004	a,b,c
(0.059)	0.40	0.082	$\gg$ 0.01	0.002	b
0.034	0.27	0.21	> 0.7	0.08	d
		0.11	0.63	0.08	e
		0.17	0.02	0.01	f
		0.073	> 0.001	0.00007	g,h
0.16	0.50	0.033	> 0.004	0.01	i

f. see reference 35

g. see reference 36

h. see reference 37

i. see reference 38

j. a number in parenthesis is from preliminary data

plotted R_2 against $(1/\chi)$ $d\chi/dc$ for the four systems
where T_c and γ data are both available. Although the
disagreement with theory is clear, the small variation in R_2 over the two decades of $(1/\chi)$ $d\chi/dc$ is en-
couraging. Apparently $R_2 = .35 \pm .15$ for all four systems; whereas, $R_{2(theory)} = 1$. Since we probably
would have assigned theoretical models 1, 2, or 3 to
one or another of these systems; it does appear as we
discussed above that the relative behavior of T_c and
γ as well as the behavior of $\chi(T)$ (low T) is the same
in the three models. From the table we see that R_1
varies by an order of magnitude while $(1/\chi)$ $d\chi/dc$
changes by 10^3 and hence there is some support for
the expected small dependence of R_1 upon model.
However R_1 should be $\sim .5$ from (48) or (49) and we
find experimentally that it is generally between .01 and
.1. This means that the χ_0 data very much over estimates the depression of T_c (and γ enhancement) apparently because we have the wrong form of $\chi(q, \omega)$.[†]
This should not affect R_2 because the integrals over
all q enter γ and T_c in the same way (λ_{spin} enters both).
Thus the factor of three disagreement in R_2 is in a
sense more serious than the more eratic disagreement
between $R_{1\,exp}$ and $R_{1\,theory}$. Nevertheless the correlation among the three parameters χ, T_c, and γ leaves
little doubt about the basic correctness of the spin fluctuations model for the many-body effects on γ and T_c
in strongly paramagnetic alloys.

We should include the observation that $c*$ experimentally is always much larger than $1/[(1/\chi)$ $d\chi/dc]-$

[†]The introduction of a finite range for the local
interaction will cause $\chi(\mathbf{q}, \omega)$ to fall more rapidly with
q which is what the experiments indicated is needed.[29]

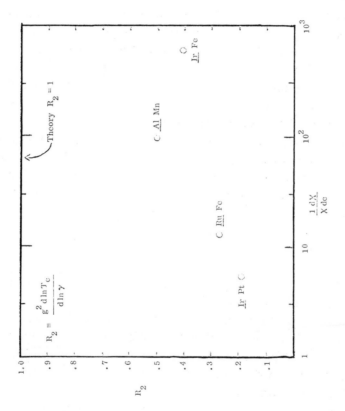

Fig. 32. The experimentally determined relationship between the specific heat mass enhancement $(d\gamma/\gamma dc)$ and the depression of the superconducting transition temperature $(dT_c/T_c dc)$
for alloys with different susceptibility enhancement $(1/\chi)(d\chi/dc)$. The theory gives $R_2 = 1$.
Data from reference 29.

generally by an order of magnitude – which indicates
that the alloys reach the f.m.i. much later than predicted by either the uniform or local model (see Eq.
(48) and (49)). This is a very serious problem and
indicates that the RPA treatment of finite concentrations is seriously wrong.[29] This does not necessarily
affect our work on R_1 and R_2 since we are treating
initial linear variations; but it raises serious questions
about our understanding of the many impurity problem.

We conclude that spin fluctuations appear to very
naturally explain the depression of T_c near the right
end of the transition metals. The theory, in fact, would
predict a larger suppression from either the susceptibility increase or (more reliably) the specific heat
increase using either the uniform or the local model.

IV. CONCLUSIONS

We have attempted to present a qualitative discussion of the superconductivity of the transition
metals. In particular, we were interested in what the
interactions are which are responsible for the superconducting pairing and also those which are inhibiting
it. We found that the strong-coupling theory using the
electron-phonon interaction seemed sufficient to explain the behavior of T_c in all but the strongly paramagnetic metals near Pd ($Z \sim 9, 10$). Even the previously
considered anomalous superconductivity in La seems
consistent with its anomalously low Debye temperature which indicates a soft lattice and large electron-
phonon interaction.

We discussed the properties of strongly-paramag-
netic alloys, in terms of several different theoretical

models, indicating the difficulty of distinguishing experimentally among the models. Then we compared the predictions from the models with the experimental results. In particular we were interested in the relationship between the specific heat enhancement (upon alloying) and the superconducting suppression because it should be model independent. The results of the analysis seemed to offer fairly convincing evidence for the importance of spin fluctuations in the metals near Pd.

Thus the presence of many-body effects from phonons and spin fluctuations (paramagnons) in the transition metals seems rather well established.

ACKNOWLEDGMENTS

I would like to thank the United States Air Force, Air Force Office of Scientific Research under Grant No. AFOSR-1149-66 for support during the preparation of these lecture notes; Mrs. Sally Nitchie and Miss Ruth Higgins for translating and typing the illegible notes into a manuscript; and Mr. Paul Chaikin for critically reading the manuscript.

REFERENCES

1. Most of the data quoted and shown here is taken from the review article by G. Gladstone, J. R. Schrieffer and the present author, "Superconductivity in the Transition Metals: Theory and Experiment," ed. R. D. Parks, Marcel-Dekker, Inc., New York, 1968.

2. B. T. Matthias, Phys. Rev. 97, 74 (1955).

3. J. Bardeen, L. N. Cooper, and J. R. Schrieffer, Phys. Rev. 106, 162 (1957).

4. J. Pines, Phys. Rev. 109, 280 (1958).

5. L. F. Matthies, Phys. Rev. 139, A1893 (1965).

6. W. L. McMillan, Phys. Rev. 167, 331 (1968).

7. P. Morel and P. W. Anderson, Phys. Rev. 125; 1263 (1962).

8. J. Carbotte, Lectures given at this Summer School.

9. A. B. Migdal Soviet Physics. JETP 1, 996 (1958).

10. J. R. Schrieffer, Superconductivity, W. A. Benjamin, Inc., New York (1964) Chapter III.

11. J. Kondo, Prog. Theoret Phys. (Kyoto) 29, 1 (1963). D. C. Hamilton and M. A. Jensen, Phys. Rev. Letters 11, 205 (1963); C. G. Kuper, M. A. Jensen, and D. C. Hamilton, Phys. Rev. 134, A15 (1964); F. F. Smith and H. L. Luo, J. Phys. Chem. Solids 28, 569 (1967).

12. T. Kasuya, Magnetism, G. T. Rado, and H. Suhl, Eds., Academic Press, New York (1966) Volume IIB, Page 255. T. Satoh and T. Ohtsuka, Technical Report of Institute for Solid State Physics, University of Tokyo, Ser. A. No. 237, Feb. 1967 to be published. A. S. Edelstein, to be published.

13. M. A. Jensen and J. P. Maita, Phys. Rev. 149 409 (1966).

14. Khanna and Rogers, Phys. Rev.

15. The references are given in reference 1 and also: M. A. Jensen, B. T. Matthias and K. Andres, Science 150, 1448 (1966); M. A. Jensen and K. Andres, J. Appl. Phys. 38, 1255 (1967); K. Andres and M. A. Jensen, Phys. Rev. 165, 533 (1968).

16. E. Bucher, W. F. Brinkman, J. P. Maita and H. J. Williams, Phys. Rev. Letters 18, 1125 (1967).

17. G. Knapp, J. Appl. Phys. 38, 1268 (1967).

18. M. A. Jensen, A. J. Heeger, L. B. Welsh and G. Gladstone, Phys. Rev. Letters 18, 997 (1967); A. J. Heeger, L. B. Welsh, M. A. Jensen and G. Gladstone, Phys. Rev. to be published.

19. R. B. Frankel, N. A. Blum, B. B. Schwartz and D. J. Kim, Phys. Rev. Letters 18, 1050 (1967).

20. N. F. Berk and J. R. Schrieffer, Phys. Rev. Letters 17, 433 (1966) and Proc. 10th Int. Conf. of Low Temp. Phys., Moscow (1966); S. Doniach and S. Engelsberg, Phys. Rev. Letters 17, 750 (1966).

21. Pascal Lederer and D. L. Mills.

22. J. Kondo, Prog. Theor. Phys. (Kyoto) 32, 37 (1964).

23. Y. Nagaoka, Phys. Rev. 138, A1112 (1965).

M. A. Jensen and A. J. Heeger, Phys. Rev. Letters 18, 485 (1967). J. Applebaum and J. Kondo, Phys. Rev. Letters 19, 906 (1967).

24. H. B. Callen and T. A. Welton, Phys. Rev. 83, 34 (1951).

25. P. Nozieres and D. Pines, Il Nuovo Cimento, [X] 9, 470-489 (1958).

26. The definition of a "repulsive" interaction requires a little care; e.g., see W. Kohn and Luttinger, Phys. Rev. Letters (1967).

27. J. R. Schrieffer and D. C. Mattis, Phys. Rev. 140, A1412 (1965). J. Kanamori, Prog. Theoret, Phys. (Kyoto), 30, 275 (1963).

28. Pascal Lederer and D. L. Mills, Phys. Rev. Letters 20, 1035 (1968). S. Engelsberg, W. F. Brinkman, and S. Doniach, Phys. Rev. Letters 20, 1040 (1968).

29. M. A. Jensen, D. J. Scalapino, S. Doniach and Pascal Lederer, to be published.

30. K. Andres and M. A. Jensen, Phys. Rev. 165, 533 (1968); M. A. Jensen, J. App. Phys. 39, 549 (1968); M. A. Jensen and K. Andres, J. App. Phys. 38, 1255 (1967); Phys. Rev. 165, 544, (1968).

31. K. Andres, private communication.

32. T. H. Geballe, B. T. Matthias, A. M. Clogston,

H. J. Williams, R. C. Sherwood and J. P. Maita, J. App. Phys. 37, 1181 (1966); T. H. Geballe, private comm.

33. K. Andres, E. Bucher, J. P. Maita, R. C. Sherwood, Phys. Rev. to be pub.

34. E. Bucher, W. F. Brinkman, R. C. Sherwood, and J. P. Maita, Phys. Rev., Letters 18, 1125 (1967).

35. G. Choutean, R. Fourneaux, K. Gobrecht, and R. Tournier, Phys. Rev. Letters 20, 193 (1968); A. I. Schindler and C. A. Macklret, Phys. Rev. Letters 20, 15 (1968).

36. M. A. Jensen, A. J. Heeger, L. B. Welsh, and G. Gladstone, Phys. Rev. Letters 18, 997 (1967).

37. J. P. Frank, F. D. Manchester, D. L. Martin, Proc. Roy. Soc. (London) A263, 499 (1961); M Daybell and W. Steyert, Phys. Rev. 168, 536 (1968).

38. R. Aoki and T. Ohtsuka, J. of Phys. Soc. of Japan 23, 955 (1967).

AUTHOR'S INDEX

Abarenkov, I., 492, 505, 507, 511
Abrahams, E., 119, 165, 697, 755, 785
Abrikosov, A.A., 21, 68, 333, 380, 387, 407, 579, 583, 587, 631, 789, 790, 796
Anderson, P.W., 419, 491, 646, 769, 859
Ashcroft, N.W., 506
Aslamasov, L.G., 126
Autler, S., 415

Bardeen, J., 227, 340, 379, 381, 382
Beasley, M.R., 420
Berlincourt, T.G., 538
Bogolyubov, N.N., 769
Blumberg, R.H., 429, 442

Callen, H.B., 904
Cape, J.A., 801
Carbotte, 378, 721
Caroli, C.M., 165, 181, 331, 342, 697, 787
Crow, J.E., 641, 651, 672, 675, 685
Cyrot, M., 680, 787

Davies, J.P.N., 420
Dayem, A.H., 741
de Gennes, P.G., 74, 389, 390, 394, 395, 408, 409, 428, 433, 436, 454, 565, 665, 675, 680, 783, 789, 814
Deltour, R., 417, 420
Douglass, D.H., 429, 442
Duke, C.B., 594
Dynes, R.C., 517, 519, 525

Eguchi, H., 683
Eisenmenger, W., 741
Eliashberg, G.M., 165, 202, 494, 761
Essmann, U., 415, 416
Everts, H.U., 599, 600

Falk, D.S., 592
Fanelli, R., 823
Ferrell, R.E., 118, 646
Felter, A.L., 322
Finnemore, D.K., 636, 641, 653, 658
Fisher, G., 817
Fowler, M., 588, 592, 608, 618
Frohlich, 227
Fulde, P., 664, 665, 814
Funnell, 694

Ganguly, B.N., 599, 600
Geballe, 266
Giaever, 417
Gilat, G., 514
Giorgi, 261
Goldman, A.M., 317
Gor'kov, L.P., 14, 21, 68, 165, 202, 230, 231, 380, 387, 392, 433, 579, 582, 631, 658, 693, 700
Gough, 694
Gruenberg, L.W., 683
Guertin, R.P., 651, 671, 672, 675
Guyon, E., 565

Hake, R.R., 538
Hamann, D.R., 593, 594, 596, 613
Harrison, W.A., 492, 504, 507
Hauser, J.J., 804

SUBJECT INDEX